SPUR PUBLICATIONS
POULTRY FANCIERS' LIBRARY

General Editors

Dr. J. Batty   Mrs. M. Batty

RARE POULTRY OF ASHE

OTHER BOOKS AVAILABLE

Poultry Culture for Profit
Rev. T. W. Sturges

Bantams and Miniature Fowl
W. H. Silk

Understanding Old English Game
Dr. J. Batty

History of Cockfighting
G. Ryley Scott

Fighting Sports
Cap. L. FitzBarnard

Ornamental Waterfowl
Lt. Col. A. A. Johnson and A. A. Payn

RARE POULTRY
OF ASHE

REX WOODS

Past President of the Poultry Club
Past President of the Rare Breeds Society

Author of
GRASMERE'S GIANTS OF TODAY

PUBLISHED BY THE SPUR PUBLICATIONS COMPANY
Hill Brow, Liss, Hampshire GU33 7PU

ISBN 0 904558 10 X

Printed in England by Calabre Printing Limited, Liss, Hampshire

CONTENTS

ILLUSTRATIONS

ILLUSTRATIONS (continued)

EDITORS' FOREWORD

There is considerable interest in rare breeds of poultry. Moreover, this extends to many countries, all sharing a common interest in reviving the many beautiful breeds of poultry which were on the verge of extinction.

The revival of rare poultry in the U.K. owes much to the dedication of a few enthusiastic fanciers. One of these, Rex Woods, has written his personal experiences and views in a manner which makes compelling reading to all who are interested in poultry.

We feel sure that this new book will be welcomed as a valuable addition to the literature dealing with domesticated poultry.

J. Batty   M. Batty

ACKNOWLEDGEMENTS

I want to thank my wife, not only for painting the two colour plates for this book, but also for lending her varied skills and energy throughout our joint venture at Ashe - without which this book would never have been written.

My thanks are also due to my son for the use of some of his photographs, as well as to *"The Field," "The Times," "Poultry World"* and Tony Pitter for permission to use theirs. Acknowledgement is given under the appropriate illustrations.

Seaton, Devon.   REX WOODS

Champion Silver-Laced Wyandotte Pullet
— with Ashe Chapel in the background

Chapter 1

"UNHINGED"

THIS is a book about poultry which might never have been written. Ironically, it was my very interest in poultry that came near to preventing it. It happened like this.

On Easter Sunday 1945 the inmates, myself included, of Oflag Va, near Heilbronn, on the Neckar, were once more in transit. The sound of gunfire from and at the advancing American troops had been growing increasingly close and audible. Finally, when hopes of the camp being over-run were high, and longed for liberation seemed near, orders were received that the camp was to be evacuated. The prisoners of war were to be transported by rail, in the customary cattle-trucks, eastwards away from the firing. To escort us out of the range of the gunfire — and of rescue — our normal guards were reinforced by the German equivalent of our Home Guard, several of whom would have been naturals for "Dad's Army".

Our route took us ultimately to the large holding camp at Moosburg, near Munich. The instructions were to travel by train at night, and to hide the train in a tunnel or camouflaged siding by day. The prisoners were to leave the train by day and be dispersed within the limits of a defined area.

On the second day, the area over which we were dispersed included a farmyard, into which we were allowed for the purpose of drawing water. On entering the yard for this purpose, the first thing I noticed was a Duckwing Leghorn hen emerging through the cat's exit at the bottom of a stable-door. Instinctively and compulsively I walked across to investigate.

On opening the door and entering, I found myself witnessing the laying of an egg, at the very moment of delivery. I rapidly stepped forward and caught this gift from the Gods in mid-air, all warm and wet. In my eagerness — I hadn't eaten an egg for

1

nearly three years — I inadvertently trod on a goose which was nesting underneath the bench on which the hen's laying-box was placed. Pandemonium erupted.

First, the goose rushed indignantly into the farmyard, honking loudly, its wings beating at the same time. The hen, partly out of natural instinct after a job well done, and partly out of panic from my rude disturbance of her act, also rushed into the yard, cackling hysterically, and causing several others to answer her.

I was the next to emerge into the farmyard, to find a frenzied German guard standing some ten yards away and aiming his rifle at me. For good measure he put a bullet up the spout, and called to me to halt and put my hands up! With the precious egg already in my trouser pocket, I readily complied. He then advanced and began frisking me, starting from the top and working his way downwards. In the nick of time, just before he smashed the egg inside my trouser pocket, I caught hold of his wrist, to prevent a messy accident. Unfortunately the guard didn't take kindly to this. He felt that I was resisting his search and he reacted accordingly, by taking three or four steps back and taking fresh aim, beside himself with fury. At that range, even shaking with rage, he could scarcely have missed. For my part I saw my best hope of survival in the prompt surrender of the offending egg. This I rapidly did, with as much nonchalance as I could muster. I still remember saying, in German, "Is this what you are looking for?" To the great relief of myself and a small crowd of onlookers who had halted their water-drawing operations, the guard seized the egg, removed the bullet from the barrel of his menacing rifle, and marched me off to the commandant. The latter was far from pleased at my "Schweinerei" — still less so when I remarked that he might have acted similarly if he had gone nearly three years without an egg! However, he had other more pressing matters on his mind, and merely confiscated my identity card and deferred final punishment until arrival at our next camp. The punishment, when it came, a few days later, was "No parole walks for two weeks" — lenient enough, especially as I was in fact on the next escorted parole walk, having borrowed an identity card from a friend who did not want to walk. On that walk I managed, while sheltering during an air-raid, to barter, in exchange for a bar of Red Cross soap, six eggs — a welcome replacement for the one that got away!

Poultry may yet prove to be the death of me, but not, I trust, before I write this book!

EARLY DAYS

My liking for, obsession with, addiction to — call it what you will — the various breeds of fowl, bantams and waterfowl manifested itself at an early age. I think this is usually the case.

Poultry fanciers are, in general, born rather than made. There may well be some in whom the urge to breed poultry for pleasure and exhibition lies dormant, until circumstances allow it to be activated. There may be others who, upon retirement, are in search of a creative hobby, who turn to the rearing and showing of poultry, and with help from other fanciers, guidance from books, as well as their own applied commonsense, discover late in life a congenial and rewarding pastime. But on the whole the urge seems to be innate — though not necessarily hereditary. In my case it certainly seemed to be the former.

I can well remember being delivered at my prep school, St. Edmunds, Hindhead, in Surrey (where, incidentally, I was extremely happy from start to finish) to the Headmaster with these words from my father: "Well, at present he knows the names of over a hundred varieties of poultry, and not much else! I hope you can teach him something besides." Well, he tried — and met with some success, to the extent that six years later I came reasonably near to gaining a scholarship to Stowe, a failure which denied me the privilege of being a near contemporary there of David Niven, with any attendant effect it might have had on my auto-biographical style. However it left me free to revert to my original intention of going to Charterhouse, which I also regarded as a privilege, and certainly did not regret.

But I can also recall the farewell words of my prep school Headmaster to my father, as I was collected from the school for the last time. They were to the effect that I would probably have achieved the scholarship, but for my obsession with poultry. What he did not mention, for doubtless he felt a certain complicity, was a most pre-occupying and distracting gift that he had once made to me. It was the 27th April 1927 edition of the National Geographic Magazine, most of which was devoted to two absorbing illustrated articles on poultry: "The Races of Domestic Fowl", by M. A. Jull, and "America's Debt to the Hen", by Harry R. Lewis. These articles and their accompanying illustrations, many of them in colour, were enough to push algebra and geometry still further into the background. I still retain the magazine in my poultry library, as well as gratitude to the Headmaster for his kindness.

Of course there were other diversions, in the form of cricket, soccer and rugger (I was captain of the school team at the last two) which should rightly share the blame with my addiction to poultry for my near miss at the scholarship.

FIRST BANTAMS

My poultry urge was not hereditary. Nor can anyone remember how and when it first came over me. But I am pretty sure that a copy of *The Feathered World* (that much lamented journal of the past) must somehow have come within my grasp at the age of seven, because it was an advertisement in that excellent weekly which launched me on my poultry-breeding career at that age.

I read an advertisement from a man in Woodhall Spa, in Lincolnshire, who was offering Birchen Modern Game bantams at "giving away price". This sounded cheap to me, and I wrote and asked what the price really was. It turned out to be one pound each, which in 1925 could be considered reasonable, rather than "giving away". Anyway, my father felt that my youthful enterprise in writing the letter should be rewarded, and I was given my first bantams, and a house and run to accommodate them in our Brighton home. I have never lost my special liking for Modern Game bantams, with their friendly disposition and thoroughbred type, as well as a pleasing range of well defined colours.

I became a regular reader of *The Feathered World* in the school holidays. My father called it the "Unhinger", the reason being that one look at the advertisements was bound to unhinge me. This was to some extent true. I liked so many breeds — and I still do — that, in addition to my Modern Game bantams, other breeds soon came into my life, Gold Sebrights, Silver Spangled Hamburghs, Blue Pekins, to name a few.

I also managed to persuade my parents to buy point-of-lay pullets of various breeds to provide household eggs. In those days crossbreds were only just beginning to oust the pure breeds as layers. Hybrids, which in turn were to oust the first crosses, had not yet arrived. The pure breeds proved very adequate for the purpose, as indeed they still are. Even in 1965 I had a Silver Laced Wyandotte pullet which laid twenty-eight eggs in the month of April. We had Barred Rocks, Buff Rocks, Black Wyandottes, White Wyandottes, Anconas, Andalusians, Minorcas, Black Leghorns, Lakenfelders, and Rhode Island Reds as layers. It was all good experience with these breeds.

But my early poultry keeping suffered from one insuperable drawback — lack of continuity caused by my disappearances to boarding school. I was lucky in that my father employed a gardener, who looked after the fowls and bantams that I left behind at the end of each holiday — "The Legacy", as my father called them. But a month at home at Easter time was not enough to lay the foundations of a successful breeding season, and, although I gained some experience and derived some pleasure, I could not hope for much success. That was to come several years later, after boarding school, after university, and after war service, when I eventually married and achieved continuity.

I'm sure this must apply to many a young would-be fancier today. I notice at shows a fair amount of interest among young exhibitors. But most of them, possibly after a taste of success in their youth, will probably have to wait until they have completed their education, and settled down, before they can achieve the continuity that is needed for more permanent success. In my case it was at the age of thirty that I was able to settle down to breeding and exhibiting poultry, and that was in South Africa, which is the subject of my next chapter.

YOUTHFUL EPISODES

Two episodes which I recall from my early days still strike me as amusing — the joke being on me in one case and at someone else's expense in the other.

The scene of the first episode was Steyning market. I had been told that Steyning market, ten miles away from Brighton, often abounded in interesting poultry being sold at auction. I decided to investigate. With a basket under my arm, and one pound in my pocket, I caught a train at Preston Park station for Steyning, where the market was near the station — mercifully, as it turned out!

Sure enough there were fowls galore, in three-tier cages running the length of a very long shed. Clearly they were mostly unwanted throw-outs or discarded has-beens, destined for rapid slaughter. But I eventually found a cage containing four fresh young cockerels with healthy bright yellow legs, and some future. I focussed my attention on these, and decided to spend part of my £1 capital on them. So focussed was my attention that I decided, while the auctioning was going on further up the line, to park myself opposite their cage, in order to be on the spot with my first ever bid at an auction. However, as the crowd edged nearer, my position became the harder to maintain. I managed to maintain it while the first adult to edge my way went round behind me. But number two was a large farmer's wife, who, noting with disapproval my disinclination to budge, said: "Will you move up — or are you glued?" Before I could explain why I was seemingly glued to that particular spot, she tested my grip on the rail with her considerable bulk. I became rapidly unglued and had to give ground.

When my chosen lot came up for sale I was still within earshot, and my somewhat distant bid of two shillings per head for the four cockerels was heard, left unchallenged, and accepted with alacrity. I felt good. Only when I went to the office to tender my eight shillings did I discover that as well as my four cockerels, I had also bought eight others in the two cages below mine, auctioned as one lot. I had already spent some of my money on sustenance and was unable to meet my financial commitments! However, my eleven-year-old face must have appeared honest, as, in exchange for my father's name and address, I was given credit.

The next snag was how to fit twelve live cockerels into a basket intended for four or less. I accepted as inevitable the auctioneer's offer to kill them for me on the spot, so that they could be packed like sardines. This was done, and so started the haul to the station, which included a testing climb up and over the bridge to my platform on the far side. The cockerels, though inert, showed a constant tendency to spill out of their crowded basket, and when I was aborded by an old codger, as I sat exhausted on a platform bench, I readily agreed to exchange eight of my succulent cockerels for four old boiler hens that he had just bought. I felt that I had a better chance of staggering home with fewer corpses to carry. At least they fitted more easily into the basket, even if the total weight remained much the same. So the deal went through.

At last the train arrived and I climbed aboard with my load. The train only went as far as Brighton, and I decided to walk down Trafalgar Street to the London Road, where a bus would take me to the gateway of our house beyond Preston Park. The walk was downhill, but I was very exhausted by the time I had carried the basket first on one shoulder, then on the other; under one arm, then the other. As I boarded the bus, the conductor told me that I could not take livestock on board his bus. I was thankful to be able to point out that my livestock were now dead stock.

My mother's initial dismay on my arrival was understandable but a hot bath, some food and bed averted the threatening tears of tiredness. Next morning a plan of action was made. My mother rang our fishmonger and poulterer, who kindly co-operated by relieving us of the unwanted corpses. The young cockerels would do for his private customers, and the boilers would probably end up in a hotel. In the end I made a profit of one shilling and eightpence! But it was not a performance I had enjoyed, nor ever repeated. However, it seemed to amuse my elder sisters!

The other episode which caused family amusement was known as "The Hippodrome Affair". I showed two of my Modern Game bantams at the Sussex County agricultural show, which happened to be held in nearby Preston Park one year. Although the bantams only achieved token recognition from the judge, in the form of V.H.C. and H.C., they seemed to interest a gentleman writing on behalf of a livestock journal called *The Hippodrome*. So much so that he wrote to me, aged thirteen, to ask if he might call and see my bantams, with a view to publishing an article, with photographs, in his magazine. He was sure that his readers would be most interested. The family motto, "Try most things once", being already a guiding principle in my young life, I readily assented. We made an appointment, and for my part I spruced things up somewhat before the great day arrived.

The gentleman from *The Hippodrome,* a journal both previously and subsequently unknown to me, duly arrived, by train from London. He was, I thought, in his sixties, and of somewhat cadaverous and sinister appearance. I conducted him round my bantams. I remember feeling at the time that he didn't really seem to know which end of a bantam was which. But he affected a certain admiration for them. So we adjourned to the house to discuss the proposed article. We moved into the dining-room for this important session — alone, though my mother, who had observed his sinister appearance with some apprehension, was not far from the keyhole, I subsequently discovered. The man seemed far more interested in discussing the photographs which were to accompany the article than in the article itself, I noticed. I soon realised why! The article would only be written if I undertook to pay for the photos. I demurred, youthfully but firmly. He tried forcing tactics, and began to foam at the mouth and splutter. I shudder to think what this abortive encounter did to his blood-pressure, but he eventually grabbed his folder, hat and umbrella, and made an undignified exit.

On his way through the hall he managed to splutter to my mother, who was having utmost difficulty in keeping a straight face, "They send me all the way down from London to interview this Mr. Rex Woods of Preston Court, and all I find when I get here is a bloody schoolboy." I would gladly have told him that, before he set out — if he had asked!

DRUSILLA'S TEA COTTAGE

My spring and summer school holidays invariably included a visit to Drusilla's tea cottage, near Alfriston, which is to the north of Eastbourne, over the Downs. For most schoolboys the tea alone would have been the highlight of the afternoon's outing. But for me the tea was just an enjoyable bonus. I was there to look at the collection of many different breeds of poultry that had been assembled. It was an absorbing sight. I remember, most vividly of all, seeing a Silkie hen in a bowl in the window of the farm produce and Sussex craft shop, with a placard in front of her: "Please do not touch me — I am hatching." Such was her devotion to duty that neither the public gaze nor the surprised comments seemed to disconcert her.

These school holiday visits to Drusilla's remained in my mind over the years, until the time came for me to embark on a venture akin to Drusilla's, and I was grateful for their inspiration.

My delight can, therefore, be imagined when, some forty years later, one evening on my return with a car load of fowls from Yeovil show, I was greeted by Michael Ann, the son of the original owner of Drusilla's, and still very much in business there himself. I was able to render belated thanks for some happy schoolboy memories.

7

Michael Ann was at that time assembling an interesting collection of the rare breeds of domestic cattle and sheep, and I was able to supply him with some Soay sheep, which I kept as mobile grass mowers at Ashe House. When, a few months later, he told me that he was anxious to re-introduce a display of colourful domestic poultry breeds at Drusilla's, I was delighted to supply him. I felt that my Drusilla story had now gone full cycle.

BLUE POULTRY

Before leaving the poultry of my youth, I must mention an Easter pilgrimage to a real fancier's Mecca of those days — the wonderful collection of Blue varieties of many breeds of fowl, water-fowl and turkeys, owned by H. Whitley, in a sheltered valley adjoining Paignton Zoo, in Devon. The collection was managed by W. Wilkinson Sen. at that time, and he was succeeded later by his son, Billy Wilkinson Jun., both of them steeped in the breeding and showing of poultry in the north of England, their interest and knowledge being spread over a wide range of breeds. Not surprisingly, they achieved for Mr. Whitley widespread success at shows, as well as great pleasure and progress at creating Blue varieties.

I had just left school, and, before going up to Oxford to take a law degree, I was working as an articled clerk in a firm of solicitors in London, in 1936. Easter was my first break, and I drove with one of my sisters down to Devon. I think I had written in advance to book a sitting of large Blue Minorca eggs. In any event, I was very well received by Mr. Wilkinson Sen., and was allowed to feast my eyes on his Blues — Cochins, Hamburghs, Minorcas, Leghorns, Orpingtons, Old English Game, as well as Blue Turkeys and Blue Indian Runner ducks. The lay-out of his grass runs remained in my mind, and some thirty years later, when I was laying out the grass runs at my Ashe House Poultry Breed Preservation Centre, I still retained the memory and idea of them. One of our first visitors was Billy Wilkinson Junior.

While on the subject of Paignton Zoo and the Wilkinsons, I recall an amusing incident which occurred at the Devon County show years later. There was a handsome Blue Orpington cockerel which won first prize in the A.O.V. Male class, from a good Silver-Grey Dorking in second place. The judge remarked to Billy Wilkinson that it had been a close thing between Billy's Blue Orpington and A. J. Major's usual top class Dorking, but that he had decided that, in view of Mr. Major's frequent successes with his Dorkings, it was now Billy's turn with the Orpington. But, alas for Billy, there were two snags — The Dorking was his, hatched from eggs supplied by Mr. Major, and the Blue Orpington was mine!

I don't know how Billy reacted at the time, but he told me the story with amusement later. So did the judge!

8

Chapter 2

SOUTH AFRICAN INTERLUDE

CONVOY VISIT

ALTHOUGH my South African interlude only spans the thirteen years from 1948 to 1961, the South African connection really began in June 1942, when I called at Cape Town in a troop convoy round the Cape.

We, the 4th Royal Sussex, as part of the 44th Division, were, so we were afterwards told, en route for Burma. But the fall of Tobruk in June 1942 caused us to be re-routed to Egypt to help form part of the El Alamein line.

After a precarious month at sea, starting with a summer's evening departure down the Clyde in late May, and a zig-zag course, including a few days sweating at anchor off Freetown, Sierra Leone, we reached the welcome sight of Table Mountain, overlooking Cape Town harbour, on 30th June. Not surprisingly it seemed like Shangri-La.

The welcome and hospitality that greeted us there made a lasting impression on many of us, and I recall, on a party at Constantia Nek with three fellow-officers, that we all reckoned that, if we survived the war, we would like to return to Cape Town. One was killed at the battle of El Alamein; of the other three, two of us did return. I did so on New Year's Eve, 1947 — and discovered that it was known locally, and perhaps logically, as Old Year's Eve.

During our three day stop at Cape Town in 1942, we had been given the opportunity to contribute to the Red Cross, to provide parcels for South Africans taken prisoner at Tobruk. Little did we realise that in four months' time some of us would be receiving the parcels to which we had contributed!

DECISION TO SETTLE

It was during the next two and a half years as a prisoner of war in company with many South Africans, some of British ancestry and some of Afrikaner stock and tongue, that I decided to go to South Africa. I feel bound to say that it makes my blood boil to find mud now being slung in the direction of these friends of mine, who were all volunteers on Britain's side, when she needed them most, many of whom have, on a personal basis, done more to help the black population in South Africa than most of their detractors will ever do.

Anyway, by January 1948 I was on my way to teach Latin, French and English, and also most school games, at St. Andrew's College, Grahamstown, in the Eastern Cape Province. My resumption of poultry-breeding was closer at hand than I had realised; for in April 1948 I married my only wife to date, and although the marriage service does not state that the purpose of matrimony is to raise poultry, it nevertheless resulted in my doing so!

STARTING UP IN THE FANCY

When I broached the subject of running a few fowls at the end of the garden, in an old lucerne patch, my wife was all in favour. She anticipated, perhaps, a pen of Australorps, which were the most widely kept of all utility breeds in South Africa then. To her surprise, a pen of Silver-Laced Wyandottes arrived. I was lucky enough to buy them from a Mr. Phillips, of Knapdaar, who had managed to import Silver-Laced and Gold-Laced Wyandottes from America the previous year, just before a total ban on the importation of stock and eggs was imposed. Within a year I had won my first *Best in Show* award, with a Silver-Laced Wyandotte pullet at the Bathurst Agricultural Show, which proved to be the start of a long association with this beautiful and useful breed, both in South Africa and in England. In South Africa I won five Blue Ribbons for the best trio of Silver-Laced Wyandottes, and three Blue Ribbons for the best single Silver-Laced Wyandotte at the five South African National shows at which I showed. I also distributed stock far and wide in Southern Africa. It was then, and has remained, my policy to distribute stock, rather than adopt a dog-in-the-manger attitude which is said to exist in some quarters — though I am glad to be able to add that, when I was gathering my collection of breeds at Ashe House, I did not encounter any dogs-in-mangers. Far from it as we shall see later.

Although Silver-Laced Wyandottes were my first and most successful breed, it was not long before I diversified. By a strange coincidence, when I first arrived in Grahamstown, by train, from Cape Town, as the train chugged slowly into the station I saw, foraging in a back garden, none other than my favourite Birchen Modern Game bantams. They belonged to a Mr. Topper, who was a water-meter reader (water is a precious commodity in Africa). One day on his rounds we began talking about his bantams, and soon I became the owner once again of my boyhood breed of bantam. What's more, they were of sufficiently high quality to win for me two firsts at South African National shows.

Next on the scene were some glossy large Black Frizzles, which had quite a story behind them. In 1951 I was travelling with a friend from the staff of St. Andrew's, as supporters of the school rugby team, which was going on tour, as was customary every second year, to Cape Town — a distance of six hundred miles. We stopped the car near Plettenberg Bay for a picnic lunch, and I happened to see among a few "Kaffir" fowls, as mongrels were then called locally, a black pullet with very well curled frizzled plumage, of light breed type and with a small frizzled crest, roaming the veld. My friend was amazed that such a sight should capture my attention to such an extent, and we proceded to Cape Town. A week later, as we neared Plettenberg Bay on our return journey, my friend said: "Don't you want to try to buy that frizzled hen?" I didn't need asking twice! We stopped, and I tracked down both hen and owner. The latter was deep in sleep in his mud hut. However, with some difficulty, but no ceremony, his family roused him from his slumber. He was quite agreeable to selling the pullet; he had a batch of younger chicks, I noticed, which included some more frizzled specimens. I also bought a smooth blue pullet of similar type, possibly a sister, as company, and also with Blue Frizzles in mind.

On reaching home, the black pullet started laying almost immediately. She proceeded to lay eighteen eggs in nineteen days. The blue also proved to be no slouch. The next task was to breed this plumage on to an Australorp body, at the same time eradicating the unwanted crest. The result was a wonderful strain of layers from the start, and by 1956 there were twenty-three large Frizzles, blue and blacks, penned at the Grahamstown poultry show, all descended from these two pullets.

Nor was this all, on the Frizzle theme. Using an acrobatic Black Pekin cockerel, I was able to create some attractive frizzled bantams, which I called Grahamstown Blacks and Grahamstown Blues. Later, with the aid of a Buff Pekin, Grahamstown Buffs appeared. They were really frizzled Pekins, with quaint frizzled crests or hoods. Unfortunately, I was not there long enough to get them standardised, though they were breeding true — as far as Mendel's law allows any frizzled fowl to do. The usual 25 per cent of the progeny were smooth, a further 25 per cent were over-frizzled, and the remaining 50 per cent were correctly frizzled. I doubt if anyone else has set about getting them standardised, though there may still be some running around on

11

South African farms. They were, I thought, decidedly attractive.

Another variation on the Frizzle theme that occurred was the creation of a frizzled version of the White-Crested-Black Poland. The white crest grew from back to front, and resembled a small white chrysanthemum. I showed one of these, a pullet, in a New Breeds class rejoicing in the name of Plettenberg Black. She created some amusement, but was not intended to be taken seriously! I also bred, showed and distributed White-Crested-Black Poland bantams, and White-Crested-Blues, one of the former winning the prize for the Best Fancy Bantam at a Cape Town National show. White-Crested-Black Polands, like Silver-Laced Wyandottes previously mentioned, and Frizzles were to feature prominently after my return to England. Experience gained with them in South Africa was to prove useful.

SHOWS IN SOUTH AFRICA

A few words on the subject of poultry shows in South Africa may be of interest. The first and salient point is the venue of the annual South African National. It is staged in a different town or city each year by the poultry club of that place. In my time it was held in Cape Town, Johannesburg, Bloemfontein, East London, Durban and Port Elizabeth. In each case it is held in mid-winter, June or July. Since my departure I hear that Grahamstown has also staged the National, which is a gratifying achievement for a club which was re-formed while I was there, in 1953. This circulating system obviously has much to commend it, if it can be worked. One hears the suggestion that our own National, now that it is run by the Poultry Club, should also move around. It does so in Germany. But in our case it can only come about if and when we can find show-holding societies willing and able to stage a full scale National.

The second point of interest is the system of classes. At the National, and other shows, there were classes in all varieties of breeds for: (a) Cocks. (b) Cockerels. (c) Hens. (d) Pullets. (e) Trios. (f) Teams of four pullets. The last mentioned often made a good display. Thus a breeder of, say, Anconas could enter in six Ancona classes with his team of Anconas. This wide range of classes usually allowed the honours to be shared; but if a breeder made a clean sweep, he or she really had cause for satisfaction. The fact that there were fewer breeds and varieties to cater for in South Africa made this wide choice easier to offer than it would be in Britain.

A third, and to my mind desirable principle followed at South African shows was that all classes in the schedule were allowed to stand, regardless of the number of entries or exhibitors. In my experience, there were no amalgamations nor cancellations. If a breed or variety failed to fill its classes, it was liable to be moved to Any Other Variety the following year. The advantage of this system is that exhibitors know where they stand, and it has been adopted by the National here since The Poultry Club, or more accurately, The Southern Counties Branch thereof, has been running it, on lines to suit club members.

Apart from these three points, South African shows were similar to ours in Britain, whether they were fanciers' shows or part of general agricultural shows.

The breeds on view naturally differed somewhat from ours, and in one notable case a familiar breed differed in type — this was the White Leghorn. They were like the American and German type of Leghorn, with smaller bodies and headgear, and much further removed from the type and size of the Minorca than our large exhibition Leghorns are.

Other differences included the existence of White Australorps as well as the Blacks that we know. The Whites, which are born blueish with slate-coloured legs, won fame in the days of laying competitions. The Blacks were more numerous than any other heavy breed, as dual purpose fowls, until first-crosses, and then hybrids, became popular. Golden Australorps and so-called "Wheaten-Laced"Australorps were also standardised, but were in my opinion not at all impressive, nor necessary.

Another dual-purpose heavy breed which caught on more in South Africa than it ever did in Britain was the New Hampshire, of American origin. Reds and a few Whites appeared at shows. Plymouth Rocks, Sussex, Rhode Island Reds, Leghorns, Minorcas, Anconas, Wyandottes, and Old English Game were also familiar breeds there.

Hardly any of the breeds eligible for our Rare Breeds classes (see Chapter 10 on Rare Breeds) appeared at South African shows, though the position may be somewhat improved now that the import ban has been eased at last. Nor were there many bantams apart from Old English and Modern Game, Pekins, a few Polands (White-Crested only) and a few Frizzles. But judging from the constant enquiries that I kept getting, and used to pass on, on my return to England, I imagine that there must be a wider selection of bantams on view now. One breed of bantam that somehow appeared on the scene was the East Friesian Silver Möwe, a German breed of Continental light breed type, and, as the name implies (Möwe means Seagull), the hens have white breasts and bellies with greyish backs and wings. The cocks have white necks and bodies with black tails. (See illustration of Continental breeds). They have the friendly temperament of the Campine.

The only local breed that I recall is Natal Game, a large strong fowl, reminiscent of Malay Game. Also, when driving through the African Territories, such as the Transkei, one saw a lot of unusual-looking colourful "Kaffir" fowls, as they were then called. They were of no recognisable or fixed breed, but they drew my attention. For my family's sake, I had to curb a dangerous tendency to brake suddenly every time I spotted one of these fowls on the horizon or outside an African hut!

Throughout my time in South Africa my poultry were a hobby and a pleasure. The sunny climate made them easier to look after. But there were two indigenous snags which had to be overcome: fowl-pox and "tampans". The former was almost certain to break out, on the comb, wattles, face and mouth, unless the chicks were inoculated at four to six weeks. Mosquitoes were the culprits. They spread the disease, which could prove fatal, by biting the unprotected parts. But the inoculation was, I found, effective. The tampans flourished in a hot climate, and were a form of mite which lurked in crevices and perches, and attacked at night. The best prevention was to have the perches suspended on wire, to prevent the tampans from crawling out of the crevices and along the perches. Early detection and treatment with dusting powder was essential.

MAKING THE BREAK

In 1961 my South African interlude came to an end. A big decision had to be made — whether to seek South African citizenship whole-heartedly, and like it, or return to Britain and complete my children's education and upbringing there. My daughter was twelve and my son nine. In both cases the decision could not be long delayed, I felt. Of course, a third course was I suppose, open to me — to remain British while continuing to accept and enjoy the sunshine, employment, hospitality, friendships and general welcome which I had found in such full measure at St. Andrew's. But this I could not regard as being in any way an acceptable course to choose. I chose England.

I imagine the reader will want to know whether my family and I have had reason to regret this big decision to uproot. I can say now, fourteen years later, that both my children, though retaining happy memories of their childhood in Grahamstown, have often thanked me for making the decision. My wife, whose paternal grandfather went out in 1854 from Wiltshire as a missionary, and later took out a bride from Dorset, and whose mother came from Monmouth, has never complained at returning to the land of her forbears. It does, however, sadden her to find such a barrage of insults hurled at her compatriots and relations almost every time she turns on the television, while anarchists and revolutionaries appear to attract no such opprobrium. For my part, I too have happy memories of my time in South Africa. But I have had to guard against nostalgia getting the better of me, and causing me to look backwards. One must focus on the future, and in 1961 my future lay in the subject of the next chapter, and indeed the main subject of this book — Ashe House.

Chapter 3

ASHE HOUSE

THE OBJECTIVES

THE notion of establishing a Poultry Breed Preservation Centre owes its origin, to some extent, to a visit to the Wildfowl Trust, founded by Sir Peter Scott at Slimbridge. I felt that, just as the species of wildfowl were gathered together and placed on view to the public at Slimbridge, thereby enabling preservation and re-distribution of wildfowl to be carried out, so there was a need for someone to do likewise with our traditional breeds of domestic poultry. I was appalled at the rapid dwindling of these breeds, and I felt like doing something about it.

From the outset the policy was to concentrate exclusively on domestic fowls and domestic ducks. This meant resisting the temptation to dissipate our efforts and resources over a wide range of species. Thus we excluded pheasants, for which in any case a Pheasant Trust was set up in Norfolk, and peacocks, which though potential crowd-pullers, were to be seen in many parks and zoos. No doubt it would have increased our tally of public visitors if we had, for instance, erected some monkey-cages on the old tilting ground, or some children's swings, or had boating on the pond, or pony-rides. But our efforts were to be concentrated where they seemed to be needed most, namely on the domestic breeds of large fowl and domestic ducks, which through modern economic causes rather than through any intrinsic fault of their own, were in danger of disappearing altogether.

This did not apply to bantams, which were, and still are, in the hands of many skilful fanciers, and had to some extent prospered for the very reasons that had reduced the numbers of large fowl — shortage of space, railage costs, and food con-

Ashe House from the Churchill Garden

The South Wing of Ashe House, from the Drake Garden

sumption. A few bantams were later included in the Ashe House collection, of breeds which were no longer to be found as large fowl in Britain, such as Frizzles and Buff-Laced Polands. But it remained essentially a collection of large fowl and domestic ducks.

In short our policy was to stand or fall by what we were doing, namely to offer to the public a display such as was not to be seen elsewhere. We ran it as we wanted it, and anyone who felt like supporting our venture was very welcome, and fortunately some seven thousand visitors a season did so.

SELECTING A SITE

So much for the idea. The next objective was to find a suitable setting for it. We realised that, to succeed, it would be vital to have an attractive lay-out. There exists the thought in many minds that the keeping of poultry is of necessity a ramshackle business. We were determined not to over-stock, nor to allow a scorched-earth appearance. We were lucky enough to find a house not only with ideal grounds for the fowls, as well as the essential pond and running water for the ducks, but also steeped in history. It was Ashe House, in the parish of Musbury, near Axminster, in Devon, the former home of the Drake family and the birthplace of John Churchill, Duke of Marlborough.

Before moving on to the establishing of the Poultry Breed Preservation Centre at Ashe House, a brief history of the place is required, because I think it is fair to assume, and it was often said to us, that Ashe House was worth visiting for its history alone.

Early History of Ashe House

Early in the fifteenth century the estate of the de Ashe family passed by marriage to John Drake of Exmouth, a cousin of Sir Francis Drake. The house was then long and rectangular in shape, running parallel to the general line of the River Axe as it flows from Axminster down to Seaton on the Channel coast. Attached to it was the Ashe Chapel, first licensed in 1387 by Brentynham, Bishop of Exeter.

The Cromwellian Wars

The story of Ashe House became linked with the Civil War between the Roundheads and the Cavaliers. In 1644, Lady Drake, a staunch Roundhead and then residing at Ashe, applied to the Roundhead forces at Lyme for a garrison to protect her property. This drew instant reaction from Lord Powlett and his Cavalier forces at Hinton St. George. They attacked the Roundhead detachment guarding Ashe, gaining access through a chapel window, routed the garrison, and burned part of the house. For this damage Lady Drake subsequently received the sum of £1,500 from the Cromwellian government by way of compensation — Lord Powlett's confiscated lands providing the funds.

It was this damaged dwelling that afforded refuge in 1647 to Lady Drake's daughter Elizabeth and her Cavalier husband, Winston Churchill, a Dorset landowner. The latter had been heavily fined for his part in the battles against the Roundheads. Being unable to pay the stiff penalty, he was obliged to surrender his lands at Minterne. So it was that, until the Restoration, the Cavalier Winston Churchill accepted refuge in the badly damaged house of his Roundhead mother-in-law.

The Churchills arrived at Ashe with two children, but the total was to reach twelve. The third child was John Churchill, who like most of the rest was baptised in Ashe Chapel. Of the twelve children only five survived beyond childhood — Arabella Churchill and four of her brothers. These four were John, who was destined to become Duke of Marlborough; George, an admiral in the Navy; Charles, a Lieutenant-General in the Army, serving with distinction at the battle of Blenheim; and Theobald, who entered the Church.

Thus it was that John Churchill, Duke of Marlborough, spent his first ten years amid the fields bordering the Axe, where curlews and seagulls frequently seek refuge from the estuary and coast, four miles away.

The Restoration and After

After the Restoration in 1660 John Drake was made a baronet by Charles the Second. In 1669 he was succeeded by his son, John, and it was the latter who decided to repair, enlarge and embellish Ashe House and its grounds. He added two long wings, thus converting it into an E-shaped building in Tudor style, in grey limestone. Sir John also dug fishponds and enclosed the grounds with a wall, thereby making Ashe House an imposing home for the now exalted Drake family.

So it continued until the last baronet, Sir William Drake, died childless in 1733. His widow survived him for nearly half a century. On her death Ashe House was let to Sir John William Pole, and in 1778 it was partly destroyed by fire. The damaged part of the house was dismantled, leaving the southern arm and part of the stem of the original "E" standing to this day, as well as the chapel, which is no longer attached to the house. Thus Ashe House is now "L" shaped.

There followed a century of obscurity and neglect until, on the arrival of a new owner, the old house was partitioned from the surrounding farm, and sold, together with the walled gardens, the fishpond and six acres, to an owner who set about restoring Ashe to its former cared-for state — though not to its former size. Thus it was that we were lucky enough to find ourselves moving into a house in good repair, and, what was more, of

Some of the free-range growing stock at Ashe
In this group are: Silver Campines, Silver-Spangled Hamburghs.
Red-Saddled Yokohamas, Buff-Laced Poland bantams,
a Barred Plymouh Rock and an Ermine Faverolle

Indian Runner ducks march past some young visitors at Ashe House

19

manageable size, thanks to the 1778 fire. We moved in, by a strange coincidence, on 6th June 1963, the birthday of John Churchill. So began a decade in the history of Ashe which was to prove of great interest to us as owners, and also, we trust, to the thousands of visitors who gained access during the years that we were open to the public.

OPEN TO THE PUBLIC

The first step in opening to the public was to obtain planning permission for change of user. No difficulty arose here.

Then came the busy task of erecting the necessary pens and enclosures. Obviously the various breeds of fowl had to be segregated, and we erected over fifty pens, of which forty were on grass; only ten, which ran the length of one of the walls of Lady Drake's garden, in an old shrubbery, were on earth. These were kept fresh with sand on top. We used large poles to support the netting to a height of seven feet, which proved high enough to keep out foxes even without the top apron which is considered necessary if a six foot fence is used. But a bottom apron, to prevent a fox from burrowing underneath, was necessary. The pens which contained Old English Game and other light breeds, such as Hamburghs, Lakenfelders, Yokohamas, Campines and Andalusians, had to be covered over with light gauge wire-netting.

For the ducks there was the fishpond, from which the out-flowing stream passed through a bog garden, and thence through six fox-proof duck breeding pens. This stream kept the ducks happy and clean at all times. Beside the pond we constructed a sightly stone-built house, with a small enclosure which projected one foot into the pond, all along one side, thus providing constant clean water for the ducks during their night-time confinement. They were easily shut into this fox-proof refuge each evening with the aid of a little corn, and were let out by ten the next morning, by which time all the day's eggs had been safely deposited in the house provided — rather than ending up in the pond, or being laid in the most carefully prepared nests which the ducks made, but which the magpies always plundered sooner or later.

In the grass pens the spring and summer growth was neatly trimmed by some movable Soay sheep, assisted by some Black Welsh Mountain sheep when the growth required urgent grazing. The latter were prone to the desire to rub against the wire-netting, whereas the Soays caused no damage and were ideal for the smaller pens. They are a sort of bantam sheep, and they have the great advantage of not requiring shearing. They shed their fleeces or coats like a bison, whose colour they resemble. I always had a booking list for their progeny, and for that of the Black Welsh Mountain sheep, when available. Both breeds were attractive, unusual and useful, and they seemed to appeal to our visitors.

But the main attraction for visitors was undoubtedly the flock of colourful fowls and ducks roaming the grounds at large. We gave to any visitor who wanted one a small tin full of corn or chick crumbs. This had the immediate effect of inducing the free-range hordes to run towards all visitors, like rats after the Pied Piper, instead of disappearing into the bushes. This kept the children sensibly occupied. The vertical Indian Runner ducks, like bottles of Hoch on feet, were a particularly arresting sight, and, apart from the occasional plundering of a tea-tray in the hands of the unwary, our visitors seemed to enjoy sharing their biscuits with expectant young Campines (they were always the most friendly), Brahmas and the rest.

There were benches along one side of the long fishpond, and it didn't take the resident duck population long each new season to realise that visitors meant food. The ducks and the Chinese and frizzled Sebastopol geese, became very tame and engaging. But the Sebastopol geese overdid things, and developed a bad habit of biting the nearest finger when the food was finished. This led to their banishment.

The assembling of the collection of the breeds was an enjoyable task for me. A start had already been made before moving into Ashe with some breeds, and I had found suitable sources of supply by going to shows, including the three recognised classics in those days: the Royal Dairy show in October, Birmingham Cattle and Poultry show in November, and the International at Olympia in December.

The policy was to breed and seek to preserve, improve where needed and distribute, some twenty breeds and varieties, as well as having trios, pairs and individual specimens of another thirty or so on view, in what amounted to a sort of poultry zoo. Of the breeds actively bred, and those represented but not bred, more anon.

SPREADING THE NEWS

Having assembled the collection, it was necessary to spread the news of our impending opening, set for the spring of 1964. The first event, which triggered off a series of other welcome coverage, was the publication in the 1963 Christmas number of *The Field,* for which paper I had previously written articles on poultry, of a two-and-a-half page article on the projected Poultry Breed Preservation Centre at Ashe House. It was excellently illustrated by *The Field* photographer Leslie F. Thompson, who came down for a couple of days to get his photographs, on this and other occasions.

While on the subject of Leslie Thompson, I must recount an

amusing anecdote in connection with him. We were photographing an Andalusian cockerel in the old disused chapel. Leslie was somewhat of a perfectionist and possessed the necessary patience to match. Photographing fidgety fowls was apt to take a long time. Eventually he was induced to click his camera for the last time. I then tried to catch the Andalusian cockerel, which had become a bit wary now. It was the best of the season's batch of Andalusians, and was due to go to the International at Olympia the following week. So utmost care was needed in catching it, by the body and not the tail. I made a tentative pass at it, but rather than risk a careless grab at the tail I withdrew my hand. "Oh! What a pity you missed him!" said Leslie, whom I had left packing away his camera, I thought. He then lunged at the cockerel and somehow caught its tail between his knee and the chapel wall. The Andalusian escaped, relinquishing the two main sickles of its tail! I was horrified and had to walk straight out of the chapel for fear of desecrating it with blasphemy. I walked round it before returning to a most apologetic Leslie Thompson.

However, if ever there was a case of "an ill wind" this was surely it. I was obliged to send another Andalusian cockerel to the show, less perfectly laced, but of a much lighter ground colour. When I arrived at Olympia, the first thing that greeted me was the substitute cockerel in its show pen with a handsome first prize card, in a class of eleven. Later I spoke to the judge, George Isherwood, who told me that he always chose a light coloured Andalusian. But for Leslie Thompson's intervention, I would have been nowhere with my darker Andalusian, I am sure. What was more, who should turn up at the show — his first ever — but my unwitting benefactor, Leslie Thompson. He felt greatly relieved, and I greatly indebted!

I was also indebted to him for the photographs that he took for the article in *The Field* Christmas number, for it sparked off an immediate favourable reaction. Early in January I had a telephone call, followed by a visit, from Tony Soper, who, among his many naturalist activities, was making films for "Animal Magic" for BBC Television. He and his wife put together an excellent film on our new venture at Ashe House, which in turn led to two other immediate television programmes.

The first was done by Ross Salmon who was the agricultural representative on "South-West at Six", for the BBC from Plymouth. Not to be outdone, and to our great delight, a camera team from ITV's "Westward Diary" descended on us, and produced another programme, with Clive Gunnell doing the interviewing and commentary. John Earle, too, on one of his adventure film journeys, canoeing down the Axe, a couple of fields away from Ashe, stopped to do some filming of the house — all of which helped our cause.

A pair of Silver-Spangled Hamburghs
with a Silver Campine hen (centre)

Indian Runner and Crested ducklings,
reared by the Old English Game hen on the left

As our opening day, 1st May 1964, approached, *The Poultry World* kindly wished us luck with an article by Betty Skewes, who came down with cameraman Ron Easton. We even appeared in the "Peterborough" column of the *Daily Telegraph,* under the caption: "Some chicken! Some neck!" an apt quotation from one of Sir Winston Churchill's wartime speeches, in view of the Churchill connection with Ashe.

Further television, radio and press coverage was to follow over the years, but this send-off was a great start and we much appreciated the favourable reaction to our efforts.

I also distributed leaflets and hanging cards within a radius of thirty miles in all likely places, such as hotels, pubs, information centres and zoos, as well as advertising in local papers.

On our opening day, a Friday, our first visitors were waiting at the gates promptly at two o'clock, our opening time. They had seen our card in a pub in Newton Poppleford — and we were in business! We had twenty-three visitors that day, and none of them wanted their money back. Quite the reverse in fact. They all seemed glad they had come. On our third day, a dull Sunday, we were relieved to see the car parks, outside the house and in an orchard, filling up with over a hundred visitors. Many took away leaflets with them, and the gospel of Ashe was beginning to spread.

It soon became clear that we could expect more visitors on a dull day than when the sun was shining. Even light rain was not a complete deterrent, though the fowls, but not the ducks, were mostly sheltering. Conversely, on bright sunny days, when Ashe and its inmates were looking their very best, holiday-makers tended to hug the coast. Another seeming phenomenon which soon became apparent was the fact that, of the seven days of the week, Saturday was to prove the least busy. It is a day of change-over, with holiday-makers either coming or going, but not, evidently, a day for much exploring, in the South-West.

Our visitors, over the years, were, with very few exceptions indeed, most pleasant, considerate and appreciative. They ranged from Women's Institute or Rotary outings, mystery tours, visits from branches of The Devonshire Association, Hard of Hearing clubs, and even a party of the partly blind. The latter seemed to get a special thrill out of holding out corn in their hands and feeling duck-bills dibbling away at it. School parties, poultry clubs from as far away as Sussex and Cornwall, a Darby and Joan club, some Cheshire farmers, choir outings and groups of foreign students all made up our heterogeneous clientele.

I remember conducting a group of foreign students from Exeter University round the grounds in person. One student, from Malaya, came up to me somewhat alarmed and informed me that one of my plants was "hostile". I was led to inspect the offending plant — a stinging nettle!

Individual visitors included, sooner or later, the vast majority, I would say, of poultry fanciers from England and Wales, and not a few from Scotland. We also had the descendants of some legendary names in poultry: a grand-daughter of Lewis Wright, whose famous *Book of Poultry* is the most prized collector's item; a grand-daughter of J. W. Ludlow, whose superb (even if rather unattainable) paintings illustrated Wright's book; and a grandson of William Cook of Orpington fame.

Overseas visitors, too, called to inspect and to buy hatching eggs. One day I was greeted by a man from Pakistan, who had successfully imported a hundred day-old chicks of assorted breeds from me a few years previously. I invited him inside, and when I enquired after his wife, he replied: "I shot her." After a pause, which left me wondering whether I had heard correctly, he added: "I was shooting tigers and my elephant moved." I didn't like to press for further details, so without more ado we reverted to talking fowls!

The few who could not have enjoyed their visit to Ashe were those who suffered from ornithophobia. In some cases this fear of feathered creatures was only discovered by surprised parents when their children were surrounded by would-be friendly fowls. I well remember the chaos of one family when one son, aged eight, was howling because he couldn't bear to be near any fowls, while his younger brother, aged six, was howling because his parents tried to take them both away from them.

Likewise, dog-ridden visitors were apt to remove themselves in a huff. For obvious reasons, dogs were not allowed out of the car park area and this led to the occasional canine scene. We lost a few visitors, but, more important, we didn't lose any chickens!

Naturally a lot of our visitors came primarily to inspect the house and grounds where John Churchill, Duke of Marlborough, had spent the first ten years of his life. As long as they did not come mistaking it for, or expecting it to match the size of, Blenheim Palace, to which John Churchill later gravitated, they seemed pleased with what they found. It was also gratifying to hear some of them say that, though they had not come to see the fowls, the latter had proved quite a revelation and an unsought bonus. Another frequent comment was to the effect that the relatively uncommercialised atmosphere was greatly to people's liking. We did our utmost to keep it that way.

I say "we", because it was very much a joint venture by my wife and me. She it was who ran "The Hatch", a hole in the wall of the converted coachhouse from which tea, coffee, and biscuits were served on trays, for consumption anywhere in the grounds.

My wife, who gained a degree in Fine Arts at Rhodes University, Grahamstown, painted all the signs which were a feature of the place. Examples of her work appear in this this book, such as "The Breeds of Ashe" and the sign which hung outside The Hatch, as it appeared in the women's page of *The Times,* illustrating an article on 5th September 1966. In the latter, the cockerel crowing beneath the signboard is of the same breed as that depicted on the board — a Red-Saddled Yokohama. On the reverse side was a Laken-felder. Another example of my wife's work was the main sign-board at the entrance to the drive. All our fifty pens had the names of the breeds painted in old English lettering, white on a black background, which enhanced the general appearance of the display.

In addition, my wife solved the problem of what to do with Ashe Chapel, which, though in good external repair, was no longer fitted out as a chapel inside. In fact it had in previous years housed a cider-press and pigs, we were told. At my wife's suggestion, we painted the walls, fitted picture rails, and made an art gallery of it during the summer months, thus providing an extra interest for visitors and a chance for artists to display and sell their work. We retained the right to veto any palpable monstrosities!

We also used the cellar of Ashe House to hang a complete set of Herbert Atkinson prints of Old English Game Fowl, and other prints and photographs, for the benefit of poultry enthusiasts.

Inside the house we opened the ground floor, with the exception of my study, to the public. Over the years only three objects were stolen: a sun-dial, a cigarette lighter, and a paper-weight. This seemed a remarkable record, in view of the thousands of visitors who wandered through. Thank Heaven we were living in the pre-bomb era then!

Two more episodes which belong to our story of Ashe House were our inclusion on Franklin Engelmann's "Down Your Way" radio programme, and a return visit from Ross Salmon for BBC Television.

One Monday in June, Phyllis Robinson, producer of "Down Your Way", passed the gates of Ashe on her way down to Seaton from Axminster station. Her task was to nose out likely subjects for Franklin Engelmann's interviews, and to pave the way for him. She was soon on the telephone to me, making an appoint-ment to inspect, that afternoon. The following day, a Tuesday, Franklin Engelmann joined her in Seaton, and was briefed by her as to his impending interviews.

The interview at Ashe took place that evening, when all was quiet — our opening hours were from 2 p.m. till 6 p.m. Franklin Engelmann had been very well briefed by Phyllis Robinson, and we were soon on the same wave-length. He outlined the sort of questions that he would ask. We then sat on the sofa, with Phyllis

The author and his wife in the grounds of Ashe House

Photo — "The Times"

Robinson holding a microphone between us. Franklin Engelmann was a far cry from those abrasive interviewers that politicians have to combat on television, and his natural good manners allied to his expertise made the interview a pleasure. I did feel, however, that, given a second chance, I could have improved my own performance considerably. But the technician, also a charming man, assured me that all pauses and fumbling for words would be easily cut. After running the recording through, he pronounced it fit for use. In the event, the broadcast on the following Sunday ran smoothly enough, apart from the usual shock at hearing one's own voice. My diction couldn't have been too good, judging by one letter that I received. In our talk I had referred to membership of the Poultry Club. A letter arrived addressed to "Mr. Woods, Poachers' Club", from someone who wanted to join!

My wife was amused to notice that, during the twenty-four hours before the interview, my main worry seemed to be, not the interview itself, but the choice of the customary music to be played at my request afterwards. I chose a tune called "Transatlantic Lullaby", which dated back to a show called "The Gate Review", which I saw three times in 1939. It was liltingly sung by Gabrielle Brune on two of these occasions, and by Walter Crisham on the third. As no recording of it by Gabrielle Brune was available, Turner Layton deputised. It brought forth a "fan" mail of one approving letter — even if it dated me, as my children thought.

Ross Salmon's return visit differed notably from the first in one important respect. This time I was allowed to devise and suggest new subjects for the camera. This enabled me to record on film a sight that I had always wanted to attempt. I was in the habit of feeding the free-range growing stock along the entire length of the drive. This was done in order to prevent wear and tear, by scratching, on the grass. By scattering the corn the full length of the drive, a distance of about a hundred and fifty yards, the youngsters were well spread out and they could all get their share without too much bullying. The idea was to shoot the opening sequence from the bonnet of the car as it drove slowly through a sea of chicken, with a gradual parting of the waves as the car advanced. The fowls were quite unperturbed by visitors' cars, and would only make way at the last possible moment. All went perfectly as planned, and some really unusual and spectacular film was taken. But at the end of the drive there was a sharp turn to the left. The car went to the left, but the cameraman went straight on, bottom first into some bushes! However he emerged in triumph, holding the camera and its precious contents safely aloft.

So much for the opening and establishment of the Poultry Breed Preservation Centre at Ashe House. Before moving on to the breeds of Ashe, in detail, I would like to record our thanks, first to Keith Sharpe, the "son" of the very successful show team R. E. Sharpe and Son, of Pilling, in Lancashire, for his help when it was needed most, as poultryman in our opening season. Secondly, our thanks go to John Arnold, a sturdy man of Musbury, who was with us from start to finish, as groundsman-gamekeeper-poutryman-shepherd. The only clash we ever had was when we both dived towards each other at the same sheep. We missed the sheep, but clashed head-on, and nearly scored a double knock-out.

Chapter 4

THE BREEDS OF ASHE

THE CHOICE

THIS is a chapter which I am going to enjoy writing above all others, because it is the breeds of poultry that have always intrigued me. Some people confine their interest to their own favourite breed, and certainly those single-minded fanciers who specialise in, and remain constant to, one particular breed are on the right track, as far as success on the show bench is concerned. But my taste has always extended to almost the whole spectrum of our colourful breeds. At Ashe I had the good fortune, granted to very few, to be able to specialise in several breeds, with sufficient time and space to allow success with most of them. It was an era of my life that I enjoyed and utilised to the full.

Before moving on to details of the Breeds of Ashe, two points should be mentioned. First, as to the choice of breeds, obviously I chose breeds which I particularly liked. That wasn't hard for one who likes nearly all breeds. But there were some breeds which I excluded on the grounds that, at the time, they did not seem urgently in need of preservation. They were breeds which could then be seen on farms in large numbers, namely Rhode Island Reds, Light Sussex, Marans, Welsummers, White Wyandottes and White Leghorns. But now their position has changed, and even these breeds have been largely driven off farms by commercial hybrids, and they have even become quite scarce at shows.

Secondly, tempting though it was to breed a much larger number of breeds, the temptation had to be resisted, or at least curbed. It was far wiser to have two or three pens of each chosen breed, in order to establish a closed flock, with several blood

The Breeds of Ashe - by Gwenllian Woods

lines, which could be judiciously interchanged, than to have one pen of each of a larger number of breeds. With only one pen of a breed, one is very soon dependent on fresh outside blood again, thus putting at risk any improvements that have been made by selective breeding.

Consequently, at Ashe the policy was to concentrate on certain main breeds, breed a few replacements of certain subsidiary breeds, and have decent specimens from leading breeders of almost all the remainder roaming the grounds on show. Later on, a few breeds of bantam were added, to enhance the collection.

CLASSIFICATION OF BREEDS

The Breeds of Ashe fell into four categories, as follows:

1. Main breeds

Silver-Laced Wyandottes	Gold-Laced Wyandottes
Partridge Wyandottes	Red-Saddled Yokohamas
Silver-Spangled Hamburghs	Silver Campines
	Black Hamburghs
White-Crested-Black Polands	White-Faced-Black Spanish
Barred Plymouth Rocks	Buff Plymouth Rocks
Dark Brahmas	Lakenfelders
Sumatra Game	Andalusians

2. Subsidiary breeds

Silver-Grey Dorkings	Blue Orpingtons
Cuckoo Scots Dumpies	Black Scots Dumpies
Silver-Laced Polands	Derbyshire Redcaps
Araucanas	Cream Legbars
White Silkies	Black Silkies
Gold Campines	Modern Langshans
White Orloffs	Bredas
French Game	Belgian Game
Old English Game — eight varieties	

3. Single specimens

Houdan	Black Orpington
Salmon Faverolle	Ermine Faverolle
Croad Langshan	Dark Dorking
Barnevelder	Indian Game
Speckled Sussex	Spangled Orloff
Buff Sussex	Blue Minorca
Black Minorca	Black Leghorn
White Leghorn	Blue Leghorn
Brown Leghorn	Exchequer Leghorn
Silver-Duckwing Leghorn	White Wyandotte
Ancona	Buff Orpington

4. Bantams

Blue Frizzles	Black Frizzles
White Frizzles	Andalusians
Silver Kraienköppe	Buff-Laced Polands
Gold-Laced Polands	Black Polands

(The breeds of ducks and geese at Ashe House are listed separately in Chapter 5 on Waterfowl.)

MAIN BREEDS

The description which follows of the main breeds of Ashe will, by the nature of things, be somewhat of a trumpet-blowing exercise, for which I apologise in advance. The very fact that they became main breeds means that they were successful, and I hope readers will forgive the pride that will inevitably emerge. I will try to keep the trumpet reasonably muted, and will only mention the major triumphs, which belong to the breed as well as the breeder.

Silver-Laced Wyandottes

In order to have a uniform flock of well laced Silver-Laced Wyandotte pullets in the field — I can imagine no finer sight for a fancier's eye — and to avoid problems of identity, although I had previously won with Silver-Laced Wyandotte cockerels, I decided, on arrival at Ashe, to keep only a pullet-breeding strain. For the layman, a pullet-breeding strain of Silver-Laced Wyandottes produced well laced pullets; but the cockerels have too much black marking on the back and cannot be shown, though for breeding show pullets they are essential. Conversely, with a cockerel-breeding strain, the cockerels are the show specimens, with the required clean silvery white on the wing-bows and the correct striping on the saddle. The females needed to produce these handsome show males, with silvery tops, will be less perfectly laced than the show pullets — and thus less pleasing to look at.

I was able to obtain foundation stock from four leading breeders, and the cross-matings that I was able to make seemed to result in a sort of hybrid vigour within the breed, which proved most revitalising. I mated up four pens of Silver-Laced Wyandottes every year. Of the four, I could count on at least three pens giving excellent fertility and hatchability.

From these pens I reared each year eighty to a hundred youngsters. The pullets were reared to maturity, except for a few poorly marked specimens; of the cockerels, all those with sunken leaders, however promising otherwise, were killed off by the half-grown stage. That was one fault that I constantly sought to eradicate — yet it was ever present. The rest were reared to maturity, when all with bad eye colour were eliminated —

another persistent fault which allowed no over-looking. I would select four or five for showing and breeding and sell the rest.

By this selection and cross-mating within the strain my Silver-Laced Wyandottes reached a high standard throughout the next decade. The most notable achievement were four pullets which were Club Show Champions at Gold- and Silver-Laced Wyandotte club shows, at Birmingham, two of which were also Champion Large Female against all breeds — a much coveted prize. Best Wyandotte (all colours) at the Royal Dairy (twice) was another landmark, as the Whites always take a lot of beating. Numerous wins at the Dairy and at the International shows and elsewhere kept the breed well to the fore.

Points to aim for in Silver-Laced Wyandottes are: a good Wyandotte head (without which, in my opinion, a bird doesn't even start to be a Wyandotte); sound lacing everywhere, including the breast, round and not pointed nor frosted at the edges; silvery hackle, not dark; clean white ground colour, the area near the tail causing the most difficulty; yellow legs; well curved original Wyandotte type (they will never attain the fluffy type now fashionable in Whites, nor does the standard require them to do so). In addition, with plenty to choose from, it was possible to improve size and colour of egg, as well as to maintain the breed's creditable laying capacity. The Wyandotte has a pleasant temperament, and this, too, received attention, with no squawkers in the breeding-pens.

Since my retirement, it has given me great vicarious pleasure to see C. Tarrant, whom I supplied with stock, winning major awards with Silver-Laced Wyandottes of such excellent standard at the main shows. They are indeed a wonderful breed, ideal for the farmyard or orchard where a respectable supply of eggs from attractive fowls is wanted.

Gold-Laced Wyandottes

Whereas my Silver-Laced Wyandottes were of a pullet-breeding strain, in Gold-Laced Wyandottes I chose to run cockerel-breeders. The show Gold pullet is admirably laced, but the conventional colour is rather dark, and she is much less striking than her Silver counterpart, at any rate in the distance. But the cockerel-breeding Gold females are of a bright medium gold colour. Furthermore they are usually well laced and can, and do, win open breeding-pen classes. Mine did so at the last International show to be held, in 1969, gaining the George Isherwood trophy for the Champion breeding-pen.

For my start in Gold-Laced Wyandottes I was indebted to the leading exhibitor, N. J. Thomas, near Truro. He sold me a fine trio, with the proviso that I would let him have the pick of my first crop of cockerels, after I had chosen two for myself. I reared twenty good ones. The day of choice arrived, and I penned them all up, and removed the two for myself, as agreed. Only a month later did I realise just how luckily I had chosen. One of the two was Club Show Champion at my first Gold- and Silver-Laced Wyandotte club show, at Birmingham. At the next two club shows it was Champion Gold male, as well as winning at the Dairy, Bath and West, and Devon County twice each. In all, my Gold-Laced Wyandottes won the cup for the Champion Gold male at the club show five times, and one of them was Reserve Champion Large Male at Birmingham, against all breeds.

They were a very popular breed at Ashe, and it was always an exciting time as the season's cockerels neared their peak for the autumn shows. In making the final selection, points to watch were: sound lacing right down the breast and under the keel; correct striping on the neck and saddle; rich yellow legs of medium length; a well-rounded tail; a good comb and eye. By using large-bodied hens of Wyandotte shape, type and size seemed to take care of themselves.

The Golds laid fairly well, but not quite as well as the Silvers, nor could much be done to achieve browner eggs from them. Tinted eggs were the best they ever managed.

Partridge Wyandottes

The Partridge Wyandotte scene at Ashe was dominated by a famous female which I was lucky enough to breed from a trio that I obtained from Mr. Alderson of Cumbria. She was never beaten by another Partridge Wyandotte, and her wins included two at the International, two at the Dairy, two at Birmingham, two at the Royal Cornwall, two at the Devon County and one at the Partridge Wyandotte club show at Ribble Valley. She started in 1967, and she was still winning at the club show at Birmingham in 1974, for Dr. W. C. Carefoot, the club secretary to whom I had sold her, in the hope that he could conjure a successor out of her. Apart from this hen, and a few decent pullets which I sold, I concentrated on cockerel-breeders, and some colourful batches of them were seen at Ashe. They were big, typical, and reasonably well marked, but rather more orange-coloured than the more favoured lemon shade of the best Partridge Wyandotte bantams. They were good enough to win a Partridge Wyandotte club show class at Launceston, and also at the Royal Cornwall, without ever reaching the standard of the Silvers and Golds. But they brightened things up at Ashe.

Andalusians

Like the Gold and Silver Wyandottes, Andalusians are a laced breed, their medium "blue" ground colour being laced with darker "blue". (I will dispense with the inverted commas from now on when mentioning blue breeds — they were merely meant to indicate that the blue is that of the Blue Persian cat, or the Kerry Blue dog, and not the blue of the sky.) Like the Laced

*The most famous fowl at Ashe—a Barred Plymouth Rock hen, winner
of thirteen first prizes and numerous championships,
with one of her sons in the background*

Silver-Spangled Hamburgh pullets

Wyandottes, Andalusians are useful as well as beautiful. Once I had got them right, they were as successful at shows as the Wyandottes.

The foundation stone of the Andalusian stud was a pullet from W. Langton (see photo) from Scotland. She was superbly laced, and all she lacked was size of body — but not size of egg, which was two and a quarter ounces, and of good shape and texture. Mated to a large male with a good head, the best of both sides was soon obtained. One more infusion of blood, from two hens from L. N. Wilding, improved the lacing, and from then on I had really high class Andalusians of both sexes to show, as the results bore out. Numerous firsts at the Dairy and the International with cockerels, which were usually fitter in the autumn than the pullets, paved the way for wider recognition, with Reserve Champions at the Dairy and Birmingham. In Breeding-pen classes, too, they made their mark, with wins against all breeds at Birmingham, the Bath and West, and the Royal Cornwall, which helped to put the breed back on the map. The females, I found, came into their own at summer shows, when they were always in lay and, being non-sitters, were available when wanted.

At lot of Andalusians were distributed from Ashe, and it has been good to see them still appearing at shows. However it would be reassuring to see more signs that they are being bred in sufficient quantity to maintain the standard. Too many hens are being shown when nowhere near ready, where fresh young pullets ought to be seen; and judging by the cockerels on view, not enough are being bred to give a good selection. I found that hatching from several pens gave a wide choice, as well as keeping the genes circulating. But Fred Hams' 1975 crop is reassuring.

Rightly or wrongly, I never used "Splashes" or Blacks for breeding. For the benefit of those who may not know, Mendel's law decrees that in blue breeds, from two blue parents, only fifty per cent of the progeny will be blue. Twenty-five per cent will be black and twenty-five per cent will be white splashed wtih blue, known as "splashes". I have read and been told, but have never proved nor disproved, that a black mated to a splash will produce a much higher proportion of blues. But I liquidated all the splashes at birth, rather than have them disfiguring the flock. Of the blacks, the cockerels were killed as soon as they were edible, and the pullets were sold as layers when ready. This left maximum housing space, and maximum attention for the blues. I found that by counter-balancing a dark blue male with light females, I could get plenty of medium blue progeny. This way it was possible to select for lacing, which is not discernable in the blacks and splashes. By selection, too, body-size, head points and tails were attended to. Legs and eyes gave little trouble.

Andalusians were very good spring and summer layers of large white eggs. But, being a Mediterranean breed, they were less prolific in cold weather than the Wyandottes, if running out, as mine were. Their hatchability was, year after year, very nearly a hundred per cent, which compensated for the number of unwanted blacks and splashes that were bound to occur. Again, being a Mediterranean breed, Andalusians required some handling and taming before they were ready to show. But I never failed to tame any that I wanted to show, and most of them showed themselves well. Andalusians were one of the outstanding successes at Ashe.

White-Crested-Black Polands

Another breed to produce champions at Ashe was the White-Crested-Black Poland. Having admired the superb specimens that Eric Parker showed, I naturally turned to him for a start. When I arrived to take a trio, his father, who was looking after them near Salisbury, refused to take payment, and merely agreed to accept a cockerel the following year in return. I mention this as ten years later at a show, Eric Parker was saying that despite the fancy prices that one hears bandied about in connection with certain breeds, he would gladly give his spare Polands away if only someone would do something with them. I reminded him that ten years ago he had done just that! And he replied: "You were about the only one who ever did!"

Anyway, I was most grateful, and turned my good fortune to immediate advantage, breeding the Club Show Champion at the Poland Club show at Olympia the following year. Other good results followed, culminating in the selection of an Ashe House White-Crested-Black Poland as Champion Large Male (all breeds) at the 1969 International. Success in breeding-pen classes, at the Bath and West and the Royal Cornwall, added further fame to the breed.

A good White-Crested-Black Poland, usually detectable at birth with a large white knob on its head, is a very hard bird for a judge to fault or ignore. If the crest is large and well formed, the tail is usually profuse and well furnished to match. Add to this a beetle green sheen and the typical Poland body shape and sound feet, and the judge's eye is caught.

Polands lay quite well, though the eggs are small. Ideally they should be kept indoors, out of the rain and mud ,but should have access to a clean lawn when the weather is sunny and dry. They pick up minerals this way, I'm sure, and the lawn grass is good for them. I found that they grew best when reared on grass, even if their adult life was to be mainly indoors. It is important to maintain vitality by rearing them under natural conditions.

For someone who wants to run a few fowls of near perfecton indoors, with a rearing and exercising lawn available, the whole unit being under close control, White-Crested-Black Polands can provide an absorbing hobby. They respond well to a high degree of stockmanship. But they are not intended to rough it on farms, nor languish half-neglected in muddy pens. Fortunately, at Ashe there were lawns for the chicks and spacious dry sheds for the adult stock. Consequently they were the focus of much attention and admiration from the public.

Silver Campines

Visitors arriving at Ashe House were often welcomed by a self-appointed reception committee, as they emerged from their cars. This committee was generally headed by some chatty Silver Campines. They seem more inquisitive and fond of human company than any other breed. If one was weeding a path or lawn, the Campines were always the first on the scene to investigate. This inquisitiveness, however, was apt to lead them into trouble. If I heard squawks of something being half murdered, as likely as not it was an inquisitive Campine pullet which had wondered what life would be like if she flew into a pen of cockerels, which had been confined in order to curb their sexual exuberance.

Silver Campines were a breed which Ashe particularly suited. They thrive on free range, being assiduous foragers. Though they can fly like pheasants, they are not wild, but very friendly. One of my favourite sights was to watch Campine pullets, which happened to be grazing at the far end of the big field, take off and fly towards me when the feed bucket was seen, and land almost at my feet.

I am indebted to my Silver Campines, too, for a chance re-introduction to the lovely Lake District. One day a visitor arrived brandishing *The Tale of Beatrix Potter,* by Margaret Lane, in which, on page 152, it states that Campines were Beatrix Potter's favourite breed of fowl at Sawrey. She is quoted as writing in a letter: "I am very fond of Silver Campine fowls. They have more character than the general run. . . . Their bright eyes are more expressive. . ." The visitor wanted a sitting of Campine eggs, which I gladly supplied. This incident prompted me to take my wife on an overdue visit to the Lake District, since when we have been there every year. The net result has been my book: *Grasmere's Giants of To-day"* — a pictorial record of recent Grasmere Sports meetings, where the characteristic Lakeland sports of Fell-running, Hound Trailing, and Cumberland and Westmorland Wrestling take place in a breath-taking setting. I was glad to be able, on one of these visits, to re-establish Silver Campines on a Lakeland farm in Easedale, near Grasmere, the farmer being a former friend of Beatrix Potter when she was in the chair at Herdwick Sheep Breeders' Association meetings.

The Ashe House Silver Campines met with consistent success

Gold-Laced Wyandotte pullets

Silver-Grey Dorkings, bred at Ashe from A. J. Major's famous strain

at the classic shows. At that time they had classes at the Dairy and the International, and six Best of Breed awards came their way, as well as a Campine Club Championship. Campines do not, however, find much favour in Any Other Variety classes at smaller shows. They look rather insignificant alongside big Cochins, or Brahmas or Minorcas. But I did have one Champion award, at Yeovil, to the credit of a Silver Campine cockerel, in his first bloom of maturity, with beetle-green sheen, as well as good barring. Wilf Allen was the judge.

Now that their breed club has petered out, Campines are under the wing of the Rare Breeds Society, and in classes at the club show, they stand a fair chance. Points that need striving for are: clean silvery hackles, soundly barred breasts, and well barred wings and tails. Silvery necks seem to militate against sound barring on the breast — a silver neck often accompanying weak breast barring, and, conversely, sound breast barring tending to be at the cost of some unwanted ticking on the neck. I always made the clear hackle the starting-point, and worked to improve the breasts, with reasonable success.

Campines lay well, the eggs being chalky white and of creditable size considering their body size and their small appetite. They hatch and rear well, if kept under healthy conditions, with partial or complete free range. They are meaty at any age, like pheasants.

Silver-Spangled Hamburghs

At the Birmingham show in 1961 David Kay, then the new Honorary Secretary of the Hamburgh Bantam Club announced that it was proposed to take large Hamburghs, whose club had become defunct, under its wing. This struck me as a good cause to support, helping to revive a most attractive breed. Ever since then large Hamburghs have had classes at the Hamburgh Club show at Birmingham, and classes were soon restored at the Dairy and the International shows.

Some very hatchable eggs were obtained from H. Beale, a Hamburgh breeder of long standing, and I was soon in a position to support the revived Hamburgh classes, with a fair share of success. In 1969 Hamburghs were added to the list of breeds at Ashe which produced a Club Show Champion, when a Silver-Spangled cockerel won this award at Birmingham. I always found it easier to turn out well matured cockerels for the autumn classics than it was to produce a pullet or hen in or near lay — though I did win with females as well.

A favourite sight at Ashe was a batch of Silver-Spangled Hamburgh cockerels which I used to assemble each year in a large open lean-to shed, from the time their final tails began to grow in September, until Christmas. Kept on clean shavings, with plenty of floor space, and perch room too, they remained very clean and fit. They could be tamed at night for the autumn shows. A constant watch had to be kept for sparring, which was always the fore-runner of fighting, and one of them had to be instantly removed before damage was done. But, while peace reigned, they were a magnificent sight.

Hamburghs proved good spring and summer layers at Ashe, of smallish but very fertile eggs. Like the Campines they were long-lived, and active foragers. They fitted well into the ecology of Ashe.

Black Hamburghs

When I started to breed a few Black Hamburghs, mainly as replacements for the collection at Ashe, little did I realise what good insurance it was going to prove. I found them particularly useful for showing under a non-specialist judge in a class of mixed Hamburghs. Perhaps judges not wholly conversant with Hamburghs, when not sure what pattern of spangling to go for, played safe and chose a really fit glossy Black. Whatever it was, I frequently had cause to thank my lucky stars that I had shown a Black as well as a more fancied Silver Spangled — notably at the Royal Cornwall, where Black females won the Hamburgh class for me three years in succession. Twice they saved the day at Olympia, too.

Black Hamburghs were neat, smart, glossy and straight forward. They were a useful adjunct to the more exciting Silver Spangled Hamburghs, and well worth their place at Ashe.

Barred Plymouth Rocks

As in the case of my Partridge Wyandottes, the Barred Rock story is largely the tale of one remarkable hen (see photo). I wasn't originally contemplating breeding Barred Rocks at Ashe, but I wanted one specimen female on view. I bought a pullet from W. J. Rich, near Tavistock, and though satisfied with what he sent me, at the time I little realised what a future star had arrived. After a year enjoying the freedom of Ashe, she had filled out beyond all recognition into a fine hen. In her third year, breaking my normal rule of showing only birds that I had reared, and reckoning that she was now eligible by residential qualification, like country cricketers, I sent her to the Royal Cornwall. She returned with a fistful of cards and fifty Player's cigarettes in her box. Amongst other awards she was Champion Large Fowl at this the largest summer show in England. Over the years — and I never over-showed her — she was to win thirteen firsts all over the country, including the International, Bath and West three times, the Royal Dairy twice (where she was Champion Plymouth Rock — all colours, large and bantam), Devon County twice (Champion Large Fowl on one occasion), and the Plymouth Rock club show at Birmingham.

41

She was one of those born show birds that walks forward to the judge almost asking for first prize. Fortunately, she had the quality and substance to back up her request, and most judges granted it. Her only snag was that she was so tame that visiting children at Ashe were apt to pick her up and damage her tail just before a show, but fortunately the busy season at Ashe coincided with the slack season for shows that I supported.

I managed to find her a worthy mate, and she bred some fair progeny (see photo) — but never her equal. Dr. W .C. Carefoot, famed for his knowledge of, and success with, barred and pencilled varieties, has been showing a large, strong, well barred female which reminds me of her. She was our most unforgettable fowl at Ashe.

Buff Plymouth Rocks

I cannot claim that my Buff Rocks were the best in the country. My only successes at the Plymouth Rock club show were gained when Will Burdett was not showing (because he was judging). But they were a particularly pleasing sight among the flock of growing stock, with their bright buff colour and rich yellow legs. I always reared a batch each season, and found them good autumn and winter layers of medium brown eggs, and of good size for table purposes. Furthermore their temperament made them a pleasure to keep.

Dark Brahmas

Dark Brahmas were late arrivals at Ashe, but, so instantly successful were they, that they hold a prominent place in the annals of Ashe. It all started when a visitor produced a dozen Dark Brahma eggs, of German strain, and offered them to me. As they were of good medium brown colour and of sittable texture, I gratefully accepted. The result was eleven chicks, all reared, which turned out to be three massive cockerels and eight lovely pullets.

It was soon clear that I had some really high class Brahmas, of size and type to compare with anything I had seen in old photographs. And so it proved in the show pen, both with me (including the Show Champion of all breeds at the Rare Breeds Society's club show, and wins at the Bath and West and the Devon County), and with good breeders to whom I sold stock, notably E. M. Rowell, H. F. Tyldesley and M. McConnell.

It is so gratifying when stock that one supplies is put to good use, just as it is disappointing when one sells good stock which is mismanaged.

Fortunately, at the same time as the arrival of my Dark Brahmas, Captain E. Duckworth and A. E. Burton in Sussex were both breeding and distributing Dark Brahmas of another good strain, so that there is every prospect of the revival of the Brahma being permanent. The more so because the Brahma club

Silver-Laced Wyandotte pullets

*Another famous fowl at Ashe — a Partridge Wyandotte hen,
winner over several years at the leading shows*

has been re-started by D. W. Ledward, thanks to whose efforts the breed has now emerged from the protection of the Rare Breeds Society and stages club shows of its own and also fills classes at other big shows. To the Dark Brahmas went the honour of winning the cup for the Champion Breeding Trio (large or bantam) at the 1974 National at Alexandra Palace, a credit to breed and breeder (H. Phillips Smith) alike.

In breeding Dark Brahmas, points to concentrate on are: in males, solid black breasts and high tail carriage, and, in females, sound pencilling, particularly on the back. Fortunately heads, foot-feather, type, size, striping and colour are all well fixed in the strains we now have. It was indeed a lucky present that I received at Ashe, to start it all.

Red-Saddled Yokohamas

Other late arrivals at Ashe were the Red-Saddled Yokohamas, to which I became considerably attached. Though not everybody's choice, for me they had several pleasing features. Though of somewhat gamey appearance, they do not require dubbing. The males have small walnut combs, and the females have hardly any comb at all, which gives their necks a slender snake-like appearance, which I find attractive. Their tails, though long and flowing, are not brittle, and on a grass run they remain reasonably intact. The rich chestnut and white of the males, and the salmon colour with white spangles of the females, make them unusual and attractive.

At Ashe they were in great favour as broodies, every hen invariably going broody before the end of March, after laying a rapid clutch of eggs with orange yolks. Once they have been tamed and handled, they make excellent mothers.

I found that they reared best in a batch on their own, not mixed with other breeds, on fresh ground. I reserved a small tongue of land alongside a clean stream for them, at the end of the drive, where I used to rear a big batch each year, usually over twenty with one Red-Saddled Yokohama hen, having amalgamated two simultaneous broods. Each morning they were sure of an undisturbed breakfast, before mingling with the other breeds; each evening they would detach themselves from the main flock and walk purposefully the length of the drive to roost in their own uncrowded house, growing more and more handsome as the weeks passed. The adult stock did well in grass pens.

As show birds the males have more potential than the females. The biggest success I had with them was when a Red-Saddled Yokohama cock was Champion Large Fowl at the Rare Breed Society's inaugural club show staged by the West Essex Society (see photo).

Points to strive for are: the correct walnut comb, which must not be pea or single, clean white tails, rich red "saddles" across the wings, and well spangled breasts in the males; in females clean white necks and tails, together with white spangling on the wings and breast, which are red-buff in colour. In both sexes, long bodies, long tails carried horizontally and well furnished, and bright yellow legs of medium length are all characteristic of the breed.

A lot of Red-Saddled Yokohamas were distributed from Ashe, but I fear that many people have either left them to rough it among other fowls, or else tried to keep them intensively without the high degree of stockmanship that this method requires. The Rare Breeds Society looks after them, giving them classes with the single-combed Yokohamas, which are known as Phoenix on the Continent, being different in type, apart from having longish tails — and even the tails differ considerably in width and texture. But these shared classes provide a welcome chance of recognition for both types.

Sumatra Game

Mention of Red-Saddled Yokohamas leads me on to Sumatra Game, for they are somewhat similar in type and tail carriage — the Sumatra being rather more robust in build, with a pea comb instead of the walnut comb of the Yokohama. With their beetle-green sheen on their black plumage, and, in some strains, their mulberry coloured faces and combs, they are decidedly smart in appearance. They also lay well and make excellent broodies. Only concentration on more intricate breeds at Ashe prevented the Sumatras from being shown more often, but with limited opportunities they were successful and always satisfactory to keep.

White-Faced-Black Spanish

Spanish, as they are usually known, interested me as being one of our very oldest breeds, dating back to the earliest days of poultry shows which began to take the place of cock-fighting when it was outlawed in 1849. Furthermore they had been allowed to deteriorate and almost disappear. They had been eclipsed and supplanted by the red-faced Minorca, both for exhibition and as a layer of enormous white eggs which could also be exhibited with success.

As a basis, I managed to obtain a Spanish cockerel, with a good white face but not much substance. The obvious mate for it was a big-bodied Minorca hen. The resulting batch of strong youngsters had hardly a trace of white in the face. Clearly another infusion of Spanish blood was needed, and a new Spanish cockerel was used. This time varying amounts of white appeared in the faces of the progeny. I put some selected pullets back to their sire, and others to a brother with the whitest face. From then on, by selection, I was able to establish a strain of Spanish that at least seemed worth having to a German fancier who

45

travelled all the way to Ashe to inspect them and purchase some Spanish eggs. They also gained a few cards in A.O.V. Light classes, and at the first Rare Breeds show in 1970, they managed to win the first Spanish class to be staged for many years.

Lakenfelders

The breeding of Lakenfelders, a German breed, at Ashe falls into two phases — the struggling infertile phase, followed, I am glad to say, by the fertile and successful phase.

At first the stock that I obtained from two or three sources was beset with infertility, to such an extent that it was a struggle to rear enough Lakenfelders for replacement purposes, let alone for improvement by selection and distribution.

But in 1969 I obtained a new German strain, and not only were all the infertility problems immediately swept aside, but a much improved stamp of Lakenfelder was produced, as the first, second and third in a class of nine Lakenfelders at the 1972 Rare Breeds Society club show proved.

After the early struggles, it was gratifying to be able to see a batch of Lakenfelder cockerels approaching maturity. With their jet-black necks and tails, separated by a white body, they were a striking sight. What was more, the new strain proved much easier to tame for show. Their type and size are that of several Central European breeds not seen here (see coloured illustration), and by no means the same as the more familiar Mediterranean type. Though Lakenfelders have never become widespread in Britain, now that a viable strain is in circulation they should have a reasonable future with the Rare Breeds Society.

SUBSIDIARY BREEDS

In some cases, the fact that these breeds were only subsidiary at Ashe reflects comparative failure, which it is now my turn to admit. In other cases they were only intended to play a limited role at Ashe, with no reflection on the breed in question. But as both catgories were part of the story of the Breeds of Ashe, here recorded, they must all be mentioned.

Old English Game

Although Old English Game were widely kept in Britain, with several clubs to foster their interests, and were thus hardly in need of preservation, I felt that no collection of poultry could be without them. So I obtained from Cumberland, from Tom Hartley, long famous as an exhibitor of Old English Game under the joint name of Greenhow and Hartley, eight pairs, and put them on display in grass runs in the chapel orchard at Ashe. The colours were: Black-Red, Light-Red male with Wheaten female, Silver-Duckwing, Blue-Duckwing, Grey, Blue-Grey, Brown-Red, and Lemon-Blue. They were a colourful sight indeed.

I used to let the hens hatch and rear a brood each, partly for replacement purposes, partly because our visitors liked to see the chicks, particularly when the cocks decided to lend a hand in brooding them (a custom which I have only met in the case of Old English Game).

It was soon discovered that my Old English Game attracted a twofold clientele, with differing motives and approaches. Each had their idiosyncracies. First there were the gipsies, who, hardly noticing any other breed on the place, made straight for the Game. Anything with white or yellow legs was ignored — they had to have dark legs at all costs. The other idiosyncracy was that, no matter what I offered, they invariably wanted the cock in the next pen. However they usually found something to their liking amongst what was offered. Secondly, fishermen, too, were drawn to Ashe by the lure of Old English Game hackles for fly-tying. They, too, had their idiosyncracies, which varied from fisherman to fisherman, and part of my job turned out to be to listen to many a fisherman's tale, or theory. Sometimes the names they used for a hackle bore little resemblance to name of the cock on whose neck it grew. However the fishermen usually managed to select what they wanted. I drew the line, however, at skinning the necks and selling capes, as they are called. Life at Ashe was too busy for taxidermy. But hackles were a profitable by-product, and kept a section of our public happy.

Araucanas

Another breed essential for the Ashe House collection was the Araucana, with its blue eggs. These eggs, which were also olive green as well as light blue in colour, brightened up the boxes of free range eggs on sale for eating, and were much in demand.

Recently, thanks to the efforts of Mrs. D. Roxburgh, who founded the British Araucana Club, the breed has at last been standardised by the Poultry Club, and, as well as laying blue eggs at home, they can now compete at shows. This is what the breed needed, and now some much-needed uniformity should follow in due course.

The British Araucana, unlike the original blue-egg fowl from Chile and the German Araucana, has a tail. It was felt that, however authentic, a rumpless version would have little appeal or future. So the British Araucana has been cast in a sensible utility mould, with all self colours as well as the colours of Modern Game standardised. Already some attractive Araucanas, notably some nice typical Lavenders, large and bantam, have been appearing with success at the shows which are giving them classes — proving yet again what a well run breed club can do for a breed.

The Araucanas at Ashe were Brown-Reds, but they tended to throw other game colours. Had the breed been standardised then, it would have been a task very much in keeping with the policy at Ashe to have joined in helping to improve, exhibit and circulate them, aiming at a greater degree of uniformity. They were pleasant fowls to keep, and I commend the idea to others.

Cream Legbars (now officially known as Crested Legbars)

Another blue-egg breed, which played a part among the breeds of Ashe was the auto-sexing Cream Legbar. If ever a breed was named to mislead, the Cream Legbar was surely it. In neither sex could I detect a cream feather, and it differs from all other Legbars by virtue of its crest or tassel, which Legbars do not have. I believe that the name may have arisen from the fact that the male chicks are a sort of cream colour at birth. Someone must have been in a hurry to name them! Since they have the Araucana's characteristic of laying blue eggs, and have a small crest like an Araucana's, why not the "Araubar"? In 1970, the Council of the Autosexing Breeds Association requested The Poultry Club to rename the breed as the Crested Legbar, which is better.

Any way they earned their keep at Ashe with a profusion of blue eggs. I would have found them more endearing if they had been less flighty — and if I had not grown tired of trying to explain away their name!

Gold Campines

The Gold Campines at Ashe were, as they are elsewhere, it seems, the poor relations of the more prosperous Silvers. Through chronic infertility they never got going in sufficient numbers to allow improvement by selection, and eventually I preferred to exploit the success of the Silvers, rather than to reinforce the failure of the Golds. This was a pity, because in old pictures the two colours, side by side, complement each other. But it didn't work out like that, I found.

Silver-Laced Polands

Another poor relation was the Silver-Laced Poland. I found them to be really a pullet-breeding variety, by which I mean that only the females were show specimens. The cockerels had far too much dirty marking on top, instead of the required silvery white. The White-Crested-Blacks put mine rather in the shade for quality, but Eric Parker, who breeds and shows both varieties, has shown that good Silver-Laced females can be achieved.

Perhaps the comparison between the two colours is not quite fair, because on the Continent they are regarded as two distinct breeds. Bearded Polands are called Paduaner, whereas the non-bearded white-crested varieties are called Holländer Weisshauben (i.e. Dutch White-crests). We group them both under the name of Poland, by reason of their crests, presumably, although there is a discernible difference in type.

I am afraid I phased the Silvers out at Ashe, mainly because the cockerels, apart from being useless for showing, were such sex maniacs! Life was quieter without them.

Silver-Grey Dorkings

With Dorkings I felt that as long as A. J. Major was still breeding and showing them, as he and his father before him have done for ninety years, they were not in dire need of preservation — the more so after Mrs. Belyavin revived the Dorking Club, appropriately enough from her home in Dorking, Surrey.

But a poultry collection without Dorkings was unthinkable, and A. J. Major kindly supplied me with some of his Silver-Greys. A few were reared with no difficulty each year at Ashe, but not in a big way. They bred easily and true, and the only two I ever showed both won at Kingsbridge. With their long deep bodies they looked stately and appropriate in the grounds of Ashe.

Scots Dumpies

Another long low breed at Ashe was the Scots Dumpy. Cuckoos and Blacks were bred from the same pen. They threw long-legged progeny as well as Dumpies, I found — as do the dwarf Dexter cattle, I gather. I liked them, and found them useful for brooding ducklings, being rather duck shaped themselves. Shortness of leg militates against fertility, but I managed to keep them ticking over, and distributed a few.

Derbyshire Redcaps

Redcaps, I feel sure, should have been fertile enough, but mine were not — at least their hatchability was not up to standard. The broad flat rose combs of the males created considerable interest, but through lack of perserverance on my part, Redcaps did not feature as prominently at Ashe as they should have. As an old breed of British origin they deserved more attention.

Blue Orpingtons

After a promising start with this beautiful breed, when, from a Black Orpington cock and a huge Splash hen, I reared a nice batch of Blues and Blacks, I seemed on the way towards establishing them. But poor fertility, thin shells which rendered many eggs unsittable, and liver cancer rampant among the few that were hatched, were the story of the next two years — and the end of my Blue Orpingtons.

How good it is to see them appearing once more at shows and winning championship awards for Will Burdett, who has obtained a strain of real Orpington type and quality. Though they have never equalled the well defined lacing of the Andalusian, Blue

Orpingtons are, to my eyes, one of the most magnificent of all our fowls, combining size, shape, colour and markings all in one.

Orloffs

If ever a breed arrived at Ashe by accident, it was the Russian Orloff. A visitor arrived with two friends, bringing with them a picnic lunch, including six hard-boiled eggs. To his surprise, on opening the egg box, he discovered that he had brought six White Orloff eggs for hatching, having inadvertently sat the hard-boiled eggs. The mistake was too late to rectify, and he offered the Orloff eggs to me. I accepted them, and duly hatched six White Orloffs.

They throve and grew big and strong, with typical almost combless heads and muffs. I found them decidedly interesting, and as I was retiring at the end of that season, after showing a trio at Yeovil, where they came second in the Breeding-pen class, I passed them on to Fred Tyldesley, in Lancashire.

Modern Langshans

I can't claim to have bred Modern Langshans at Ashe, but I did help to do so. Ian Kay, president of the Poultry Club in 1974, sent me a lovely reachy Modern Langshan cockerel which he wanted mated with a black Belgian Game hen of mine, with a view to introducing some tightness of feather into his Modern Langshans. Some strapping youngsters resulted, and were passed on for further experimenting. The Modern Langshan cockerel was a pleasure to own, with his tight glossy plumage, reachy body and whip tail. His crossbred progeny laid the same almost pink shelled eggs as pure Modern Langshans lay. They have a small amount of shank feathering, unlike the German Langshan, which looks to me like an Australorp on stilts, and is also a most striking fowl.

Bredas

Another very subsidiary breed at Ashe was the Breda, a Dutch breed, rather like black Sultans with the same vulture hocks, but without the crest. They had no combs, nor any great claim to beauty nor utility. Their placid temperament made them welcome at Ashe, but they were not fertile enough to bother about, I felt, though a few were bred.

Silkies

Silkies were not in great need of preservation, but they were naturally needed at Ashe, where they proved great favourites with the general public, with their furry plumage. Blacks and Whites were on show. My original intention was to run a flock of them as broodies, but the Yokohamas, Sumatras and Scots Dumpies usurped them in this function, proving more waterproof and equally frequently broody.

50

French Game

French Game made their appearance at Ashe following a surprise gift of eggs. They were large birds, somewhat between our once popular Modern Game and our Old English Game, I would say. Mine were Black-Red in colour. Though they were quite imposing and enhanced the display, I did not breed them in any quantity.

Belgian Game

Another species of Game from across the Channel, the Belgian Game, was on view at Ashe. They appeared to me rather like Malay Game in size and countenance, but with a sort of triple comb, and without the curved back which is characteristic of the Malay. Nor was the tail carried with the Malay's downward arc. Belgian Game look quite fierce, but were pleasant fowls to handle. My males were Brown-Reds, and the females were either black or black with golden necks. Like the French Game, they were more for show at Ashe than for general distribution. On the whole I was not in favour of the indiscriminate spreading around of obscure breeds, but preferred to help revive and distribute breeds already known and in need of attention. Having said this, the very next breed that I shall describe, in the Bantam section of this chapter, is a notable and, I hope, worthy exception to this principle, namely the Silver Kraienköppe.

BANTAM BREEDS

Ideally, with time and space permitting, it would have been nice to have seen each breed of miniature fowl alongside its larger counterpart, where both existed. It would have provided a useful comparison. But, having elected to concentrate on large fowl, the bantam breeds only appeared, as time went by, for various special reasons, as follows:

Silver Kraienköppe

When Silver Kraienköppe, a breed which originated on either side of the German-Dutch border about 1925, were introduced at Ashe, they had not then been seen in Britain as large fowl, as far as I knew. Nor had they reached the show bench in bantam form. So when I was offered some eggs, on the "try most things once" principle, I entrusted them to the nearest Yokohama, with excellent results.

By the time I had reared them, I had decided that they would be a welcome addition to our breeds of bantams, on several counts. In the first place, their Silver-Duckwing colour and marking were of good standard; in addition, they had outstandingly attractive tails, well rounded and well furnished; they had neat heads with walnut combs and minimal wattles, and thus achieved a slightly gamey appearance without the aid of dubbing scissors;

furthermore, no excuses were needed concerning their size — they were natural bantams. Finally, they responded well to pen training.

The Silver Kraienköppe made quite an impression at Ashe, and also at shows when I put them on display. Now that the German standard for the Kraienköppe, Silvers and Golds, has been adopted by the Poultry Club, judges can familiarise themselves with the breed, and exhibitors can know what to aim at. Furthermore, the Royal Cornwall and other shows in Cornwall, as well as the Rare Breeds Society, have been putting on classes for them. So the chance of a future is there if sufficient breeders are interested. I certainly distributed enough to that end.

The main points to aim at are: in males, solid black breasts; pure silver top colour; striping in neck and saddle; neat walnut comb and minimal wattles; long body and well-rounded tail. The female's colouring and marking are much like that of the Silver-Grey Dorking.

I wish I had had a longer time in which to get to know them. My first impressions were entirely favourable, and I was glad I was able to circulate them quickly, before I retired. Had the large Kraienköppe been available, as it seems to be now, since both Silvers and Golds have appeared at shows, I would certainly have found room for some at Ashe.

Andalusians

One of my themes in articles for poultry journals had been that all worthwhile breeds should be bantamised if they were to survive. It was in an effort to practise what I had preached that I embarked on Andalusian bantams. Of the Mediterranean breeds, the Leghorn in most of its colours, the Ancona and the Minorca had all been successfully bantamised, and were prominent at shows — even if, through economic circumstances, the large fowls were dwindling. The Andalusian, however, though appearing sporadically, had never been really established in bantam form, and I set about helping to fill this gap.

Already W. Langton had made a good start at bantamising Andalusians in Scotland, and with two hens from him, and a cockerel from elsewhere, a start was made. To improve the lacing and the ground colour, some large fowl blood was infused, with partial success. But much more work remains to be done. So far it has proved difficult to attain sound lacing, the desired shade of medium blue ground colour, and real bantam size, all on one bird. But the goal is within sight for several breeders who are working on them. Furthermore, the vital incentive has been provided, first by classes staged by the Rare Breeds Society, and then by a class at our largest all-bantam show at Reading, and then by the National. These chances must not be missed by default.

Buff-Laced Poland bantam pullet, five times a winner in five attempts at leading shows, including Birmingham and Reading

Blue Frizzle bantam hen, winner of six consecutive first prizes in 1972, and still winning in 1975 (Bath and West)

Andalusians brought great fame to Ashe, and I was glad to be able to devote some effort towards launching the long overdue Andalusian bantam.

Frizzles

The motive for introducing Frizzle bantams at Ashe was to put this peculiar plumage before the public. As large Frizzles were not any longer to be found in Britain, I had to resort to Frizzle bantams.

On the Continent Frizzles are not a breed, but merely a feather variation, found and allowed in Japanese bantams. But in Britain they have long been standardised as a breed, the type of which is well removed from that of the Japanese. Frizzles must have broad and short backs, round full breasts, and moderately short legs. Though the tail must be carried high, a long tail is listed as a serious defect. With frizzled Japanese now admitted to the standard, in order to fall into line with the Continent, it seems more important than ever to keep well away from the Jap type when breeding Frizzles.

I fancied Blue Frizzles, and from a White male from A. W. Mills, and a Black female from J. C. Spargo, two of our foremost Frizzle breeders, a flying start was made, and some nice Blues appeared, as well as some Blacks and Whites (not splashes, rather surprisingly). H. Easom Smith in his book *Bantams for Everyone* writes that a good Blue Frizzle takes a lot of beating in the show pen. This I can most certainly endorse. I have four Blue Frizzle hens which take it in turns to go to shows, according to their other engagements, such as rearing two broods of chicks for me each year. Between them they have scored ten firsts out of a possible twelve, at the leading shows, including Champion Bantam at the Rare Breeds club show, Best Ornamental at the Cornish Bantam Fanciers show at Wadebridge, Best of Breed at Alexandra Palace and two firsts at Reading in large classes — yes, one of them was under H. Easom Smith! Some good Blacks have also been bred, notably the Champion Bantam at the West of England Championship show at Newton Abbot racecourse, and the Champion Bantam trio there the following year.

One has to breed a lot of Frizzle chicks, because, with Mendel's Law at work, from two heterozygous Frizzles one gets only fifty per cent properly frizzled. Twenty-five per cent are over-frizzled (homozygous, I imagine, but horrible to behold), and twenty-five per cent are smooth. I dispose of all the over-frizzled and smooth specimens as soon as they are edible, and then sit back to enjoy the properly frizzled flock growing up. They are hardy, easy to rear and good layers, many of mine laying brown eggs (rare in bantam breeds), which I encourage by selection.

Frizzles are quaint and attractive, especially on dry sunny days.

On damp wet days they lose their curl, but soon regain it. At Ashe they were not everybody's choice, but they had their share of admirers and I was glad that I included them. I really should have made some large Frizzles, as I did in South Africa, but time ran out.

Buff-Laced Polands

Buff-Laced Poland bantams found their way into the collection at Ashe by virtue of their colour, which at the time was only available in England on the quaint body of the Poland bantam. They are buff with white lacing, a rare combination in poultry, known, but only recently revived in Britain, in the Wyandotte. With laced breeds very much in vogue at Ashe, I added this delightful colour to the collection, and the Buff-Laced Poland bantams soon won a host of friends.

Every year I used to run a large brood in Lady Drake's walled garden, and visitors sitting in the sun with their tea-trays were soon sharing their biscuits with the Poland chicks, which grew tame and confiding in these secure surroundings.

They laid surprisingly well right through the spring and summer, and the eggs hatched readily. Most of the chicks reared well, apart from a few which succumbed to a sort of cerebral meningitis it seemed, which caused them to lose control of their neck muscles. I never bred from any that recovered, and as the years went by, so did the incidence of the disease almost disappear. In winter they were better off inside, to avoid constantly soaked crests, but they were active and needed no coddling, I found.

The Buff-Laced Polands did well in the Laced Poland classes at the Poland Club show, being rather better laced and smaller than the Gold-Laced and the Silver-Laced. My constant aim was to reduce size, as they have on the Continent. Other points to aim at included: an even buff ground colour, with distinct white lacing; a well-laced globular crest, with a full beard and muff; wattles and V-shaped combs must be eradicated by selection, in the males. The chief snag in showing Laced Polands is that, though the standard permits some white in the crests of birds more than a year old, some all-round judges do not know, and others, understandably perhaps, do not tolerate, this concession. I won mainly with pullets, for this reason. I had one particularly lucky pullet (see photo) which won every time I showed it, five in all, and all of them large classes, including Birmingham, Reading and the Bath and West. She was one of those birds that was always alert when the judge was around — a priceless attribute which can make a good bird lucky as well.

Gold-Laced Polands

These are gold with black lacing. They first appeared at Ashe as a by-product of the Buffs, and, as they went well together, they were added to the list. They were an additional attraction, but they were never as well laced, nor as sound in their ground colour, as the Buffs.

Black Polands

All-Black Poland bantams, with beards and dark mulberry skins, as distinct from the White-Crested Blacks, with no beards and white skins, were also added, and very smart they looked. Their crests were far easier to keep clean, than those of the White-Crested varieties, and their dark skins, as seen also in Silkies, as well as in White Polands, were distinctive. With no large counterpart available, they were worth their place at Ashe in bantam form, I felt.

Champion Male at Olympia, 1969 — all breeds
A White-Crested-Black Poland from Ashe

Chapter 5

THE DRAKES OF ASHE — AND THE DUCKS

FROM the very first day that Ashe House, former home of the Drake family, was opened to the public, visitors were wont to remark that the Drakes of Ashe had now been replaced by ducks! Certainly the ducks were very much at home on the seventeenth-century fishpond which Sir John Drake had dug at Ashe.

When looking for a suitable place in which to establish the poultry breed preservation centre that was envisaged, an expanse of clean water was essential. The fishpond at Ashe, ninety yards long and fifteen wide, fed by a swift-flowing trout stream, was ideal.

The stream is known as the "Warlake". "Lake" is apt to mean "Stream" in Devon, we discovered, and the "War' referred to was a battle which took place about eleven hundred years before we arrived on the scene. Invading Norsemen, who had landed at Axmouth, four miles away, were met by the defending Saxons, who had lined up on the high ground nearby. The invaders were repulsed, and the Warlake is said to have run red with Norse blood. Anyway, it was back to normal by the time we and the ducks moved in.

The Policy

Although ducks were to be very much an integral part of the activities and attractions at Ashe, there was to be no attempt to ape the Slimbridge Wildfowl Trust, where the many species of wildfowl are so well presented. At Ashe the idea was to fill a gap by concentrating on the domestic breeds of duck, which, though kept by individual members of the British Waterfowl Association and others, were not on show at Slimbridge, nor anywhere else, it seemed.

The choice of domestic breeds is nothing like as wide, nor are they as colourful as the wild species. But they made an interesting collection, and many of them were new to visitors. I obtained most of the breeds from the Priory Waterfowl Farm, at Ixworth in Suffolk, which had been taken over by Lt.-Col. A. A. Johnson from Reginald Appleyard, one of the greatest names of domestic duck breeding. Lt.-Col. Johnson was assisted at that time by John Hall, who is one of our leading waterfowl exhibitors. Between them they fixed me up with some excellent pairs.

Drake Trouble

Anyone who thinks, as I half-thought, that pairs of domestic ducks can be kept in a flock on the water in a large enclosure, needs to think again. I realised that they were promiscuous, and that to breed any particular breed it would be necessary to pen that breed up separately. For this purpose six breeding pens were constructed, with a stream running through them all. But on the pond I had reckoned without the extreme randiness of the drakes!

At the first approach of spring, I noticed that the ducks were no longer swimming — and on the water, swimming, was precisely where I wanted them to be, looking in their element. I soon discovered the reason. As soon as a duck was rash enough to venture on to the water, a sort of aquatic "gang-bang" (I believe it is sometimes called) took place. No wonder the ducks were remaining ashore!

There was only one thing for it. The drakes were incarcerated, and used only as needed. With the pond situation thus sorted out, the ducks, accompanied, but not unduly molested, by a few lucky drakes, returned to the water and resumed their entertainment of our visitors. They grew very tame, and gave much pleasure.

The ducks living on and around the pond had to be confined to the pond area, which was bordered on one side by a row of Lawson's Cypress and on the other by Silver Birch and Beech trees alternately. This was soon found necessary in order to prevent them from spending the entire day shovelling up the mash which was available for the growing chicks elsewhere. A 2 ft. wire-netting fence was sufficient for this. The ducks received a handful of pellets each morning, and a handful of corn each evening, plus a bonus from the hands of visitors.

Rearing ducklings

The pleasing prospect of having broods of ducklings swimming on the pond with their mothers was tempting, but it would have been courting disaster, even if the ducks could have succeeded in hatching their eggs.

In the first year, I allowed two Buff Orpington ducks and a White Crested to attempt to hatch. The Buff Orpingtons nested in hiding under the Lawson's Cypress trees, making a sort of

The seventeenth century fishpond at Ashe House,
fed by a swift-running trout-stream

Buff Orpington ducks

blanket of down and dead leaves, which they pulled over the eggs whenever their left the nest to feed. But plundering magpies eventually tracked down the well camouflaged nests, and made a feast of the eggs.

The White Crested, however, laid her nine eggs under a holly bush at the end of the pond, and the magpies, no doubt deterred by the prickly leaves on the ground, did not plunder the nest until very near the hatching day. With six eggs left intact, the White Crested duck brought off six ducklings. Rather than allow her to walk or swim them to death on the pond, I played safe and let her rear them in an enclosed duck pen.

Not wishing to invite further disasters, in subsequent years I entrusted the hatching and rearing of ducklings to hens, using mainly Scots Dumpies, Silver-Grey Dorkings and Laced Wyandottes.

The Indian Runner ducklings were allowed to run free, after a few days to get going. They are by nature nervous creatures, but with a tame hen they soon gained enough confidence to take food from visitors' hands. In fact the Runners did rather well in this respect, using their height and reach to advantage over others.

It was not advisable to have too many ducklings at large, because they made such a mess of the chickens' water and mash. So apart from the Indian Runners, most of the other ducklings were reared in a former sheep assembling enclosure, surrounded by a 3 ft. stone wall, in a central place, near the back door. As they grew, they were moved first to the duck pens, and eventually to the pond when ready and able to cope.

Predators

Fortunately, the presence of human beings at Ashe was enough to keep marauding foxes away during daytime, but at night everything had to be either up a high tree, or safely shut in. The ducks were easily shut into their waterside enclosure when they were fed in the late afternoon. They were let out at ten o'clock in the morning, by which time they had laid their eggs in a communal nest inside their house. The idea of letting them make their own nests around the pond was abandoned in the first season, owing to the double threat of magpies and foxes.

The only time that a fox succeeded in getting at the ducks in their night enclosure was when the pond froze, and the fox was able to walk on the ice and stampede two ducks into putting their heads through the wire-netting which was frozen into the water. The fox duly beheaded them. Ironically enough, it was soon after this and a couple of other fox episodes elsewhere that I was invited to contribute to the Axe Vale Hunt. I reckoned that I already had!

Over the years the fox depredations were kept to a minimum. Judging by the number of fowls and ducks that I supplied as replacements for foxes' victims, I feel we got off lightly. But it was a constant battle of wits.

Mink only arrived on the scene right at the end of our time at Ashe, mercifully. As it was, a mink squeezed its way into the ducks' night enclosure, where the last five Buff Orpington ducks were awaiting collection by their new owner. Two were fatally chewed about the neck. The suspicion which fell on the mink was confirmed when three were trapped next to the scene of the crime.

To exclude mink from any enclosure is not easy, especially as they do not confine their attacks to night-time. Mink would have taxed the ingenuity of our poultryman-gamekeeper, John Arnold, to the full.

Rats could have made themselves most objectionable, had we not been surrounded by Ashe Farm, which employed a rodent exterminator. As it was, rats only appeared on our ground spasmodically, and they met a hot reception from John Arnold with his traps, and my son with his gun.

Hedgehogs, too, were on the black list at Ashe. But deportation rather than liquidation was the rule in their case. They found our fowl houses, which were raised one brick high off the ground, tempting places underneath which to site their own nests, and any house that had remained in one position for several months was liable to reveal a nest of hedgehogs when lifted.

Though welcome inmates in most gardens, hedgehogs were not an asset where broods of chicks or ducklings were being reared. Despite their otherwise pleasing nature and habits, they were addicted to wrecking hens' nests and eating the contents, whether eggs or chicks. When this had happened twice in Lady Drake's walled garden, which had until that point been regarded as a fox-proof and vermin-free sanctuary, with the culprit caught red-handed on the second occasion, hedgehogs were declared non grata.

Consequently, whenever I encountered a hedgehog on my twilight locking-up rounds, I would shine my torch on it, which made it curl into a prickly ball. Out would come my pocket handkerchief, which would be spread on the ground next to the hedgehog. With the side of my foot I would roll it on to the handkerchief, the four corners of which I gathered together and thus lifted the prickly hedgehog without getting pricked. Thence the hedgehog, still spherical, would be deposited into a bucket and driven by car to "Hedgehog Corner", my own special dumping ground for redundant hedgehogs, about a mile away from Ashe.

The average annual total of deportations, which only occurred in summer, was about a dozen. But still they appeared. So we decided to mark one with a small blob of paint. Four nights later our suspicions were confirmed when the light of my torch fell upon yet another hedgehog near the entrance to the main drive. It had an unmistakable blob of blue paint on its backside. Clearly I was dealing with a homing hedgehog! This time I escorted it one mile in the opposite direction. This subtle attempt at disorientating the animal appeared to be successful, because no more hedgehogs with blobs of paint were recorded at Ashe. But the hedgehog supply never ran out.

While on the subject of hedgehogs, I recall one rather embarrassing incident. One very hot summer's night, when doing my lock-up round, I left my jacket in the house, with my handkerchief in the pocket. When I came upon a hedgehog, I found myself without the usual means of lifting it. I improvised, by removing my shirt and using it to lift the hedgehog. As the car was in use elsewhere, I decided to hoist the hedgehog up a high embankment across the road from our main gate. I intended to hang on to one end of the shirt, but somehow the hedgehog went sailing over the top of the high bank shirt and all. I was left standing naked to the waist in the middle of the road, with numerous cars fixing me in their headlights. This continued while I clambered on all fours up the steep bank in pursuit of my shirt. I was quite relieved when the next edition of the local paper contained no mention of any night-time nudist in the district. Streakers had not yet revealed themselves in those days!

A female stoat with young caused brief but extensive havoc one year, taking a total of twelve growers in the space of two days. She was liable to pop up anywhere, attacking her victims by the throat. Fortunately she obligingly returned to the carcase of one of her victims, where our poultryman, Keith Sharpe, was waiting for her with a gun. Other stoats appeared occasionally, but they all seemed to be merely in transit, luckily.

The last villains on our list were a pair of ghoulish crows. They attacked any chick or half-grown youngster with a white head. The prime targets were the White-Crested-Black Poland growers, after the hen had left them. Even with the smaller Buff-Laced Poland bantams around, the crows made straight for the White-Crested-Blacks. To thwart the crows, the White-Crested Polands had to be reared in covered runs. Then the crows demolished the head and neck of two ten-week-old Brahma cockerels (the pullets have darker heads). After a lengthy vigil one of these perverted crows was shot and the other steered clear.

Badgers

Before leaving the subject of predators, this seems a convenient place to tell the tale of our two badgers — Brock and Roll.

My son, who was a keen schoolboy naturalist at the time, had taken me badger-watching on Musbury Castle, the site of an old

Soay sheep trimming the grass in the pens

Badgers' breakfast — or was it their supper?
Being nocturnal, they spent most of the day sleeping it off

Roman encampment overlooking the Axe. We carried out twilight vigils at their holt, ready to hold our breath when they emerged. But we didn't have to! They must have used the back door. Though there were unmistakable signs of very active badgers all round the promontory, no badgers emerged from the main entrance which we were watching.

So, when two orphaned badger cubs were offered to us, one April, we readily accepted. In future all badger-watching was going to be easy and comfortable.

The cubs were about three weeks old, with their eyes open and in good condition — one boar and one sow. They were soon induced to feed on milk from a bottle, and later on bread and milk, and thence to a diet of household scraps. They throve on this, as indeed they should have done, judging by the tempting smell of the badgers' brew. On several occasions I came into the kitchen, from working outside, and whiffed an appetising smell on the stove, only to be told that it was for the badgers.

In many ways it was like rearing puppies. The badgers lived in a convenient stone-floored outhouse (known forever after as the "badger house"). At eight o'clock in the morning they received their breakfast, consisting of toast and gravy — which they, with their nocturnal minds, probably regarded as supper. At all events, after re-arranging their new straw bedding, which they received daily, they usually retired to bed for the day. They were most fussy about their bedding. No matter how or where it was put for them, they invariably went through the ritual of re-arranging it to their liking. They were also strong on hygiene. They clearly regarded one particular corner of their abode as the lavatory, and this we cleaned for them daily. Throughout the hot summer, not a single flea or bug took up residence on or near the badgers. They were as clean as any dog.

At about nine o'clock in the evening all that summer, after the fowls and ducks were safely shut up, badger-exercising time began. They were always ready to scamper out and run all over the grounds of Ashe. I well remember the look of surprise on the face of a friend who came up the drive and reported that he had seen two badgers romping in the mown hay. This was one of their favourite games, while the hay was available. Another favourite game seemed to be to come full tilt at my wife or me and charge slap into our legs. My wife always wore her wellingtons for badger-exercising!

After half-an-hour of this romping, Brock and Roll were called into the kitchen, and they never needed calling twice. After sniffing up towards their meal on the stove, they would follow one of us into the badger house, where each had its own dish, to avoid barging and bickering.

The badgers appeared very happy with this routine, and evidently regarded their house as their holt. For, one night they managed to force their way out, through the wire-netting front. At eight o'clock in the morning they were safely back inside, sound asleep, after a hectic night out, no doubt. The wire-netting was replaced by chain link, to prevent further escapades.

That summer with the badgers proved interesting and enjoyable. However, we had only adopted them on our "try most things once" principle, and by the beginning of August there were signs that their welcome would soon become outstayed. In the first place they had grown to the size of Cocker Spaniels, and while remaining friendly and controllable, they could not be handled. The boar, in particular, was apt to snap if one tried to pick him up, and a corrective slap did nothing to prevent him from snapping again next time. Secondly, we did not want to keep them as pets for ever, yet we did not want to release them anywhere near the fowls and ducks of Ashe. Fortunately we had a waiting list of people who wanted them for various reasons. Then one evening they signed their own deportation order.

The last thing I want to do is to blacken the name of the badger, but to anyone who defends them by saying that they do not bother to take poultry or pheasants, I can only say that mine demolished the first bantam they ever came across. They needed no parental tuition.

The twilight outings of our badgers passed off without mishap, until one fatal night in early August the inevitable happened. A Black Wyandotte bantam hen had managed to nest in Churchill garden, in a box hedge. In our attempts at finding her we had been singularly unsuccessful — but not so the badgers. Blood-curdling screams were heard, and I rushed to the scene, to find the boar badger chewing her up. A hefty kick in the ribs made him relinquish his hold and scurry into a rose bed. But when I picked up the dying hen, Brock rushed at me, snarling. Only a timely, harder, kick in the ribs halted him in his tracks. Five minutes later, when I had disposed of the dead bantam, they were blandly reporting at the kitchen door for their legitimate supper, as if nothing had happened. But it had — and I wasn't going to let it happen again.

The following afternoon, each in a tea chest, Brock and Roll were on their way to a home on Dartmoor, to share a life with two other pet badgers. So ended the summer of the badgers. It had been fun while it lasted, but it had lasted long enough. It had certainly given us all the badger-watching for which my son had craved. But we didn't try it twice.

For anyone who doesn't know, here is the Concise Oxford Dictionary definition of a badger: "Grey-coated, strong-jawed nocturnal hibernating plantigrade quadruped between weasels and bears. . . ."

So now you know! But just in case you are stumped by "plantigrade", it is an animal "that walks on its soles". Like us?

THE DUCK BREEDS OF ASHE

The breeds of domestic duck kept at Ashe fall into three categories, as follows:

Middle-weights:

Buff Orpingtons
White Crested
Cayugas

Blue Orpingtons
Blue Crested
Silver Appleyards

Light-weights:

Black East Indians
White Call Ducks
Silver Appleyard Bantam Ducks

Indian Runners:

Whites
Blacks
Fawns

Before turning to the above breeds that were kept at Ashe, mention should be made of other breeds of domestic ducks which were not included and the reasons why they were not. The two heavy-weight breeds, the Aylesbury and the Rouen were omitted. The Aylesbury, being the white table duck par excellence, is familiar to most people. The Rouen, being the colour of the common Mallard, is a magnificent sight when in full plumage, but, as with the Mallard, the male Rouens go into eclipse in summer, and just when we would have been wanting them to look their gayest for our visitors they would have been looking drab. The Khaki-Campbell, a middle-weight, is the popular duck kept commercially for laying, and therefore not in need of preservation.

Finally, it was reluctantly decided to exclude the Muscovy, which is really a species apart. For a start, Muscovies take thirty-six days to hatch, against twenty-eight for the other breeds of domestic duck. Secondly, Muscovies, though large and heavy, especially the drakes, can fly. They usually make their nests out of harm's way. They are therefore useful on general farms, where, in return for home grown corn which they can scavenge, they will rear batches of ducklings with a minimum of super-vision or attention. But at Ashe anything which could fly into other fowls' pens are excluded, and Muscovies, despite their friendliness, came into this category, as did Peacocks and Guinea fowl.

Buff Orpingtons

The Buff Orpington duck, like the fowl of the same name, was created by the late William Cook of Orpington, Kent. It is an ideal all-purpose breed, for eggs, table, ornament and exhibition. The females are a lovely shade of even buff, whereas the drake's

Silver Appleyard bantam ducks

Photo — "The Field"

head and neck are a delightful seal brown, terminating in a clearly defined line. They have orange legs, feet and bills.

They lay white eggs in good number, and are excellent medium-sized table ducks. They have a pleasing disposition and look good on the water. Buff Orpingtons were, perhaps, the most popular duck at Ashe. They also won at shows.

Blue Orpingtons

The Blue Orpington, unlike the Buff, has a white bib, well defined. They should be an even blue all over, apart from the bib, which is not easy to achieve. White in the flights of the drakes is permitted by the standard. They threw some Black Orpingtons, also with white bibs. Both were attractive.

White Crested

In body-shape and size Crested ducks resemble the Orpington which means that, besides its quaintness, the Crested is a decidedly useful breed of duck. The Whites are the pure Chinese white of the White Call Duck, with rich orange bills, legs and feet. The crests on top of their heads, like round snowballs, make them most attractive.

Not all the ducklings were born with crests, and only those born with centrally placed crests of a reasonable size were retained. Apart from the slight danger of putting their heads through diamond mesh wire-netting, and then being unable to withdraw, owing to the protruberance of the crest, the Crested were easy and satisfactory, as well as being unusual. Furthermore, they proved most successful when shown in Any Other Variety Duck classes, catching the eye of the judge and public alike.

Blue Crested

These were to all intents and purposes Blue Orpingtons with crests. They bred some Black Crested, and both had white bibs. They did not breed very true, a large proportion of the ducklings lacking crests. But enough were bred for replacement purposes, and they enhanced the beauty of the pond collection.

Cayugas

The Cayuga, a black breed of duck, is named after the lake in North America, whence it was imported into Britain in 1871. The bright green sheen of the Cayuga Drake has to be seen to be believed. It really is an emerald green, and there must be no purple tint.

My Cayugas laid rather dusky greyish eggs in fair numbers. Their chief drawback that I discovered was the appearance of some white feathers after the first moult, which increased with age. Large black ducks were a novelty to many of our visitors.

Photo — Tony Pitter

Chinese Gander

69

Silver Appleyards

The large Silver Appleyard is a handsome and useful duck, whose plumage is difficult to describe (see photo). Roughly, the females are a much lighter and more silvery version of the Mallard in colour, and the drakes have bright green heads and necks terminated by a white ring, reddish-brown breasts and silvery bodies. The progeny varied in shade. I stuck to the paler shade, which fitted the name of the breed.

Silver Appleyard Bantam Ducks

These were of the same colour as the large Silver Appleyard, but about a third of the size. They were of a lighter build.

Black East Indians

Almost as iridescent as the Cayuga, the Black East Indian drake is like a more horizontal bantam version. Mine laid eggs varying from almost black to grey and olive green, the same duck's eggs undergoing this change as the season progressed. They matched the Silver Appleyard Bantam Ducks for size and type, and looked well in their company. Both needed pinioning to prevent them from flying out of their enclosure.

White Call Ducks

These were rounder and slightly smaller than the above two light-weight breeds. Their white plumage was of the purest imaginable tone, and they stood out among the flock on the pond. Their round heads, with bright orange bills, were most appealing. They, too, could fly out of bounds if not pinioned.

Indian Runners

The main point of Indian Runners is for them to be seen running, with their bodies and necks bolt upright. So there was no point in keeping them with the main flock on the pond, where they would have looked like any other duck when afloat. They were somewhat less messy and gluttonous than other breeds, and their presence in the grounds, on parade like soldiers, outweighed the necessity of cleaning and re-filling the water fountains that they dirtied.

Indian Runners are reasonable layers of large green eggs. The ducklings adopt a vertical stance from the second day onwards, and a brood of them on the march is an engaging sight. They are a good breed for anyone who has no pond, and wants something slender and amusing to watch, with a fair supply of duck eggs as a bonus.

Runners are more nervous than other breeds, but, if fed out of one's hand from birth, they will continue to do so, I found.

At Ashe there were Whites, Fawns and Blacks. Whites have always been the most popular, and usually of the highest standard, but some Fawns are tall and slender enough to hold

A Blue Crested drake disrupts a pair of Buff Orpingtons at Ashe

Photo — "Poultry World"

Some breeds of domestic duck at Ashe

Silver Appleyard duck (large variety); White Crested duck; Cayuga duck

their own at shows. My biggest thrill from showing Indian Runners came at Yeovil show, which was noted for its display of waterfowl, when a Black drake won the Indian Runner class, against Whites and Fawns. Alas, like the Cayugas, the handsome Black Runners tend to grow white feathers on the breast from the second year onwards.

GEESE

A pair of Chinese geese shared the pond with the main flock of ducks, lording it over them with great dignity and very little aggression. They were decorative and friendly, and useful grass-mowers along the banks of the pond. Ching and Ming were their names. They were not allowed to increase in number, but Ming used to lay about thirty eggs a season, which proved fertile when hatched by other people.

The introduction of a pair of Sebastopol geese, a white breed with frizzled plumage, was less successful. They started well enough, and were much admired. But I began to get tales of the small corn tins, which were issued to visitors, being rudely snatched and tossed into the pond by the Sebastopols. Finally, one little girl had her finger painfully mistaken for a worm, with blood to prove it. I checked on this, and confirmed personally that it was only too easy for blood to be drawn in this way. So to prevent further carnage, the Sebastopols were banished.

Chapter 6

THE POULTRY CLUB AT WORK

A CENTURY OF ACHIEVEMENT

A Brief History

THE birth of The Poultry Club, as we know it today, took place on 14th November 1877, at the Crystal Palace. I do not propose to embark on a detailed history of The Poultry Club, which could be very dry reading. Although history can be interesting, I like mine as modern as possible. Accordingly, after a brief historical preamble, I shall pursue the general policy of this book, which is to write of my own involvement with the affairs of the Poultry Club. That way I should at least know what I am writing about.

Although our present Poultry Club dates back to 1877, there had been a predecessor, which started in 1863 but only lasted for three years. However, during that short life it notched up one notable achievement — the world's first book of poultry standards, in 1865. America followed with its first *Standard of Excellence* in 1867, incorporating ours with alterations and additions.

The need for these standards had arisen as a result of the outlawing of cock-fighting in 1849. A new form of pleasure from poultry was already starting, in the shape of poultry shows. The earliest recorded purely poultry show was held in the grounds of the London Zoo in 1845, and the first Birmingham show for poultry was in 1848. With the abolition of cock-fighting, poultry showing gained rapid impetus. The need for a standard to judge by soon became apparent.

It is interesting to note the breeds which made up this first book of standards. They were: *Large Fowl:* Cochins, Brahmas, Malays, Game (nine varieties), Dorkings, Hamburghs (five varieties), Spanish and Polish. *Bantams:* Game, Sebrights, Rose-combs (Blacks and Whites). Ducks: Aylesbury, Rouen, Black East Indian and White Call. Geese: Toulouse and Embden. Also Turkeys.

This modest list, apart from reminding us which are our oldest breeds, clearly indicates what an important and voluminous task lay ahead for The Poultry Club in connection with the passing of standards for breeds which were shortly to burst upon the scene. For the stage was set for the entry of a whole host of new breeds, such as the Plymouth Rock, the Wyandotte, the Langshan, the Orpington and the Sussex — and, at a later date, the Rhode Island Red. Many breeds were to arrive from the Continent. All require standardising, and throughout The Poultry Club's first century the guarding of the standards has been one of its chief concerns, and remains so today, as a glance at the most recent Poultry Club Year Books will confirm.

The era of exhibition poultry was at hand, and was to continue in its heyday until the First World War. Between the two World Wars commercial poultry began to share the stage and then to dominate it. But shows continued side by side with laying trials. After the Second World War, commercial poultry-keeping became an industry, based on hybrids, food conversion rates and controlled environment. Poultry shows re-started and once again provided pleasures for lovers of pure-bred poultry.

In many cases the post-war shows were staged by commercial concerns, with the exhibition poultry included somewhat on sufferance, mainly to provide the necessary live element and the "noises off". Now with the poultry industry in relatively few, though all-embracing, hands, the commercial poultry industry and the exhibition poultry Fancy have gone their separate ways. Those who keep poultry for pleasure, and regard showing their stock as part of that pleasure, must do so under their own auspices. The result of this has been The Poultry Club's greatest achievement to date, namely the running of its own National Show, first at Nottingham in 1973 and subsequently as part of The London Small Livestock Show at Alexandra Palace — with not a broiler nor battery hen in sight. We had achieved self-reliance.

THE AFFAIRS OF THE POULTRY CLUB

In paragraph 2 of the General Rules of The Poultry Club the objects are clearly stated, as follows:

> "The objects are to advance in every possible way the keeping and breeding of pure-bred poultry and in particular:
>
> (a) To keep up-to-date the British book of poultry standards and to govern the administration of new breeds to standardisation.

(b) To foster international collaboration in poultry matters, to co-operate with specialist breed clubs, formulate rules for the conduct of shows and provide panels of qualified judges, and a breeders' directory.

(c) To promote a public consciousness of the work of British pedigree standard poultry stock.

(d) To encourage, assist and advise domestic poultry-keepers.

(e) To assist and actively support all kindred poultry organisations."

This seems a suitable juncture at which to review the ways in which these objects have been, and are being, pursued by The Poultry Club. It will be seen that on all counts the pursuit has not been in vain, nor wide of the mark.

Standards

From the very start, the standards have been one of the main concerns of The Poultry Club. As recently as 1971 the third edition of *British Poultry Standards* was published by Iliffe Books, edited by C. G. May, a former editor of *Poultry World,* organiser of the live poultry section of the International Show for many years (until it ceased in 1970), and a member of the Poultry Club Council. A sub-committee met Mr. May and provided information and help in his revision of this important work.

Since the publication of this edition of *British Poultry Standards,* mainly thanks to The Rare Breeds Society, several more standards have been passed by The Poultry Club, and these will be included in the next edition, I trust. Meanwhile they have been published officially in recent *Poultry Club Year Books.*

New Breeds

At one time the creation and eventual standardisation of new breeds entailed such a lot of work that there was a Standards Committee to deal with all applications. Stringent rules were laid down to ensure that any newly created breed would in fact breed true, and these rules still apply today. But the volume of applications has, since the Second World War, dwindled almost to vanishing point, and all matters to do with the Standards are dealt with by the Council, which will set up sub-committees as required.

The era of newly-created breeds seems to have passed, and the emphasis is on preserving what we have, rather than on adding to the list. Before and after the First World War new breeds such as the York, the Golden Essex and the Wyndham Black were standardised, and the machinery still exists for admitting any worthwhile new creations that may be presented. But, judging from the lack of popularity and apparent extinction of the above breeds, and others, any prospective new breed is in for an uphill struggle.

Ready made breeds from the Continent, such as the Barnevelder, Welsummer and Marans have fared much better. With them and other breeds from abroad the policy has been usually to adopt the foreign standard, used in the country of origin. A recent example of this is the admission of the Kraienköppe, a breed of German-Dutch origin. This policy has been in operation throughout the first hundred years of The Poultry Club's existence, and has given us a great variety of breeds to add to the short list of breeds in the original book of standards in 1865.

Specialist Breed Clubs

As I write, in 1975, there are forty-four specialist breed clubs affiliated to the Poultry Club. These are the backbone of the Fancy, and to those honorary secretaries who run their breed clubs efficiently great credit and thanks are due. The well-being of their breed is in their hands. They co-operate closely with the central body, and when a breed club decides upon an addition or alteration to the standard, the amendment is submitted to The Poultry Club for approval and ratification. The Poultry Club, as guardian of the Standards, will make sure that the change is warranted, and not the sudden whim of a hastily convened meeting in some out-of-the-way hall, before assenting. But the wish is to co-operate harmoniously on this and other matters with breed clubs.

Since 1969, when The Rare Breeds Society was founded, every breed now in effect has a breed club. For those breeds which lack their own breed club are now catered for by the Rare Breeds Society, which is in turn affiliated to The Poultry Club. This has given renewed hope of survival to many threatened breeds, and the venture forms the subject of a later chapter.

International Collaboration

Over the last hundred years International collaboration has taken place whenever the chance has arisen. In the past, often through The Poultry Club, British stock has been exported abroad, and foreign breeds have made their way here. But in recent years fowl pest restrictions and import regulations have hampered collaboration of this nature. But one of the most enjoyable and successful forms of collaboration took place in 1971, when a Poultry Club party visited the famous Hannover Show. This, too, forms the subject of the next chapter.

Show Rules

One of The Poultry Club's earliest tasks was to formulate show rules, to apply at all shows held "Under Poultry Club

Rules". These rules were last revised by a sub-committee in 1967, and are available to all show organisers. They were also printed in the 1971 Poultry Club Year Book.

Judges' Panel

Also dating from early times and continuing into the present is the Judges' Panel, which provides a list of qualified judges to officiate at shows. The subject of judging as well as the workings of the Judges' Panel is also dealt with in another chapter.

Breeders' Directory

Throughout the history of The Poultry Club there have been various forms of Breeders' Directory. At present newcomers and other intending purchasers of stock can find a comprehensive list of members who will supply stock in the *Poultry Club Year Book*.

Domestic Poultry-Keepers

Nowadays the members of The Poultry Club are predominantly domestic poultry-keepers, as opposed to large scale commercial poultry-keepers. Between the wars this was not so much the case, and it was found desirable to have classes at some shows confined to domestic poultry-keepers, in accordance with one of the declared objects of The Poultry Club. Though the need for these special classes has disappeared, this object is still pursued, in that The Poultry Club is run for the benefit of its members, the vast majority of whom are domestic poultry-keepers.

Kindred Poultry Organisations

The most notable kindred poultry organisation is The British Waterfowl Association, and there has always existed mutual assistance and support between the two of us.

In addition, there are some ninety poultry societies, most of them show-holding, affiliated to The Poultry Club. Rosettes and other awards are offered by The Poultry Club at many of their shows as an appreciation and encouragement for the work that these societies perform.

PERSONAL INVOLVEMENT

At the Ashe House Poultry Breed Preservation Centre the policy was to participate in the poultry show scene, particularly in winter, when a day spent indoors at a poultry show is a welcome refuge and enjoyment. This participation was to lead to a far greater involvement with The Poultry Club than I had ever imagined.

My involvement in Poultry Club affairs started when I was voted vice-president in 1966, and thus automatically president elect for 1967. Until then, though a keen member of The Poultry Club, my main energies had been directed towards establishing and running the Ashe House Poultry Breed Preservation Centre, as well as a considerable volume of poultry journalism. The latter consisted, at that stage, mainly of illustrated articles for *The Field,* and breed articles and show reviews for *Poultry World* — both activities being aimed at filling a small part of the gap left by the departed and much lamented *Feathered World.*

I assumed that my election as president was more on the strength of what I might do, than for what I had already done. Accordingly, my first contribution was to take over, when asked, the editorship of the *Poultry Club Year Book,* from Harold Easom Smith, who had edited it in the first two years of its revival, 1965 and 1966. As it was I who had risen to my feet at the A.G.M. in 1964 pleading for its reintroduction, I felt that the least I could do was to agree to edit it. I did so for the next five years, before handing over, with every confidence and excellent results, to David Hawksworth in 1972.

The next thing that struck me as requiring attention was the method of appointment to the Poultry Club Council. Although the existing Council deserved our gratitude for the way in which its members conducted the club's affairs, I felt that a more democratic method of election to the Council would get a wider range of members interested and involved in its running. Until then a place on the Council was reached in one of three ways: (a) By invitation from the Council. (b) By being voted president by all the club members. (c) By being an area representative.

Of these routes, (c) had become partly disused, because not all parts of the country had area branches any longer. But there were still some Council members who had reached the Council by this route. Anyone elected via route (b) was vice-president for a year, before automatically becoming president, to enable him or her to learn the ropes, presumably.

I arrived by route (b). No doubt some admirable choices were inducted along route (a), but when it was put to Poultry Club members at the 1967 A.G.M. (which was actually held in February 1968, at Reading Show, because the International show, at which it was normally held, had been cancelled owing to foot-and-mouth disease — which may seem an odd reason for cancelling a poultry show!), the feeling was overwhelmingly in favour of a revision of the system.

In future, both the president and the vice-president were to be elected annually by postal vote of all members who cared to exercise their right to vote. The president can only be elected for a total of three consecutive years in all. He must then stand aside for at least one year, to give someone else a chance. In addition, six Council members retire in rotation each year, after four years' service, and are replaced by six more elected by a members' vote. Retiring Council members may stand for immediate re-election and, if re-elected, they miss no Council meetings in the process, thus keeping valuable continuity.

This new system has certainly resulted in the election to the Council of representatives from up and down the country, including, most importantly, some from Scotland. Obviously the more distant Council members cannot be expected to attend as many meetings as they would like. But they are able to do a lot for The Poultry Club and its members in their area. With this in mind, the minimum number of attendances annually at Council meetings stands at one, not counting any held on the day of the A.G.M. Clearly it is a waste of everybody's time to to stand for election if there is little prospect of being able to attend enough meetings to keep abreast of decisions made. Fortunately there is a nucleus of Council members who make a point of getting to nearly all the meetings, thereby maintaining continuity and keeping the affairs of The Poultry Club ticking over. In order to let the voters know who these "regulars" are, attendance figures are now published before election time.

Having been president in 1967 and again for a three year stint from 1969 to 1971, I was automatically debarred from standing for election in 1972. Nor have I done so since — it is the turn of others. But I have been happy to continue on the Council, and have been re-elected to do so. Council meetings are not the wildest form of excitement, but they are necessary. Now let us examine what goes on at them.

A TYPICAL COUNCIL MEETING

Poultry Club Council meetings are normally held in January, April, July, September and November, with the A.G.M. nowadays held in February, since the cessation of the International in December. They are, with the exception of the November meeting, held in London, occupying a two to three hour session, starting at 2 p.m. When feasible, the November meeting has been held at Birmingham Show, in order to enable more distant members to combine the show with attendance at a Council meeting. On the whole it has been found that Council meetings conducted at shows, though useful for the reason just mentioned, or for some urgent business, are somewhat rushed and noisy — competing against the surrounding roosters. More relaxed and reasoned discussion takes place at London meetings, with no distractions.

Obviously Poultry Club Council meetings vary in their subject matter, but by and large they follow a fairly constant pattern.

The agenda usually runs something like this:

1 Apologies for absence.
2 Minutes of the last meeting.
3 Matters arising from the minutes.
4 Finance.
5 Correspondence.
6 New and re-joining members.
7 Judges' Panel applications.
8 Year Book.
9 Any other business.

The first two of the above items are self-explanatory, and are soon dealt with. It is when the third is reached that red-herring time is apt to begin, with points that really belong elsewhere in the agenda liable to lead off at a tangent. But the chairman will keep the discussion to the points which actually arise from the previous meeting, which must be cleared up.

And so to finance. This looms larger at some meetings than at others, but the current situation is always reported and noted. Future policy is kept under review.

Under correspondence, letters received by the secretary, which require the Council's attention and instructions, are dealt with. These may include complaints, suggestions, offers of help, requests for information or assistance, and queries about the standards.

The ratification of the applications of new and re-joining members has, in recent years, consistently proved to be the bright spot of any Council meeting. It makes the Council members feel that their journeys have been worthwhile, when they hear that an appreciable batch of new members has been attracted to the club. When Shelagh Jones took over as secretary in 1965 the membership stood at 687; now, in 1975, the figure is 1817. Long may this upward trend continue to cheer our Council meetings. Only another one hundred and thirty-eight thousand needed and we shall reach the figure of the German Poultry Club's membership!

Judges' Panel applications are now dealt with by the Council. Previously they were handled by the Judges' Administration Board, of which the Reverend J. C. Eddy was for many years chairman. It held its meetings twice a year, usually at the beginning or the end of a Council meeting. This tended either to keep Council members who were not on the Judges' Board hanging around waiting, or else caused them to hurry through Council business in order to make way for the Judges' Board. Furthermore, it was felt that a wider spectrum of knowledge and opinion such as is now available on the Council would be advantageous, and that more frequent meetings than the Judges' Board's previous two per year, would help in dealing with an increasing volume of applications.

Applications are considered, and tests are conducted as required by experienced panel judges, and it is on their recommendation and advice that the Council deals with each case.

The *Poultry Club Year Book* has become such a vital part of the Poultry Club's functions that it is frequently an item on the agenda, either to review the balance on the last edition, or to sanction the expenditure and fix the timing schedule for the next.

Any other business tends to become rather hurried, but it is a most important item on the agenda. It gives all Council members the chance to raise any point that they or their constituents, as it were, may wish to pursue. Often points raised under Any Other Business will be put on the agenda for the following meeting, allowing time and further thought meanwhile, and ultimate fuller discussion.

So, at about 4.30 p.m., ends a typical Council meeting. The Council is responsible to Poultry Club members for conducting the affairs of the club, and deals with most matters that arise by a majority decision. But certain matters are considered by the Council to warrant, or are laid down in the Poultry Club Rules as warranting, reference to all members at the A.G.M. The raising of subscription fees, for instance, come into this category of matters which require to be tested by general consensus at the A.G.M.

SUB-COMMITTEES

There are no longer any standing sub-committees, but certain matters are referred to *ad hoc* sub-committees, whose members go into a subject or scheme in greater detail than would be possible at a full Council meeting, with other business to get through. The sub-committee will in due course report back to the Council, and decisions will be taken by the Council in the light of the sub-committee's report.

Serving on sub-committees can prove arduous and expensive (in rail fares) for those who volunteer to serve. Though the preliminary work may be done by correspondence, subsequent meetings usually take place at shows, or before or after Council meetings, in order to cut down travelling expenses.

In recent years the revision of Poultry Club Show Rules, in 1967, and of Poultry Club Rules, in 1971, were both the result of sub-committees. As I write, a sub-committee under the chairmanship of David Kay is examining the desirability and feasibility of a Poultry Club ringing scheme. It is a big task, and those who agree to serve deserve our gratitude.

SOME NOTABLE ACHIEVEMENTS OF THE LAST DECADE

I suppose that the Poultry Club's most notable achievement in the last decade is the fact that it has doubled its membership in that space of time. And it is pretty obvious where most of the credit for this happy state of affairs must go — to our excellent secretary, who has conducted the day-to-day routine of the club with such cheerful efficiency. There are, however, certain achievements which stand out as landmarks in the club's recent history, and I list them in chronological order:

1965 *The Year Book*, which had lapsed since 1954, re-started. As well as providing members with their own medium for their articles and photographs and advertisements, and breed clubs with space for free publicity, it also attracts and guides newcomers, and reaches many lands.

1967 *Poultry Club Show Rules* revised, to suit modern circumstances and to guide exhibitors and show organisers.

1968 Election of president, vice-president and Council members reorganised, thus opening up the possibility of service on the Council to all members.

1970 *Poultry Club Rules* revised, and published in the Year Book of the following year.

1971 Fowl Pest discussion at the Ministry of Agriculture, concerning the resumption of shows. This was an important occasion for all exhibitors of poultry, who had suffered a curtailment of their activities for nearly a year, through no fault of their own. The discussion took place at the Ministry of Agriculture, Whitehall Place, on 11th August. Those present were: Mr. A. C. Sparks (the Minister's representative), Mr. W. E. Mason (i/c Animal Health, Division I), Mr. Kelly (Veterinary Department), A. R. Woods and W. Burdett (President and Vice-President of the Poultry Club).

Will Burdett and I were courteously received, and the important outcome of the meeting was that the Ministry was able to differentiate between exhibition poultry and poultry kept under commercial conditions. Accordingly shows were resumed that autumn. This difference must be maintained, now that it has been established, so that we are not made to suffer through the misfortunes of others. In our turn we undertook to co-operate in the Ministry's vaccination scheme, and did so gladly.

1971 Poultry Club party to Hannover Young Bird Show. (See the next chapter.)

1973 Poultry Club National Show held at Nottingham in February. Following two financial disasters early in its history, the Poultry Club had not regarded itself as a show-holding organisation. But with the end of two of our three main "Classics", the Royal Dairy and the International, immediate action to replace them was felt to be imperative. Hence the birth of our own National.

In the autumn of the same year, thanks to the initiative of The Southern Counties Branch, our second successful show was held at Alexandra Palace, and repeated in 1974.

MEMORABLE NAMES

Although, as stated at the beginning of this chapter, it has not been my intention to linger on the past, but, rather, to review the present, it would be unthinkable to close a chapter on The Poultry Club without reference and reverence to three of its most illustrious names. They are two former presidents and a former secretary: W. Powell-Owen, Capt. E. H. S. Duckworth and Mrs. Celia Duckworth, whose names are almost synonymous with The Poultry Club.

My arrival on the scene was after W. Powell-Owen's day, but one only had to talk with the older members to realise what a legend his name had become. The period of his greatest influence was during and after the Second World War, during which he did so much to keep our pure breeds going. To his memory our utmost thanks are due.

Captain Duckworth's association with The Poultry Club spans very nearly the whole of its first century. There are not many fanciers who can win, at the age of five, in 1897, and be still doing so in 1975! As well as turning out a prodigious number of winners (and also some losers with good grace), Captain Duckworth has served The Poultry Club for many years, including four years as president, before retiring from the Council in 1974. He was honoured by a special luncheon, arranged by the Southern Counties Branch, to mark his eightieth birthday in 1972. His sheer stamina must surely be a source of inspiration to us all.

While her husband was breeding and exhibiting his poultry at Copthorne, in Sussex, Mrs. Duckworth devoted much time and energy to the administrative side of the Fancy, first in the Poultry Offices at the Royal Dairy and the International shows, and later, from 1958 to 1965, as secretary of The Poultry Club — a task which she took over on the death of W. H. Silk, another famous Poultry Club name. They all deserve our deepest gratitude.

PRESIDENTS OF THE POULTRY CLUB OF GREAT BRITAIN DURING ITS FIRST CENTURY

Lord Sherborne, 1881-82
S. Lucas, 1883-85
Earl of Verulam, 1886
R. A. Boissier, 1887-91
L. C. R. Norris-Elye, 1892-1901
L. C. Verrey, 1902
R. T. Thornton, 1903
H. Wallis, 1904 and 1911
C. Seabrook, 1905
Viscount Deerhurst, 1906
Col. S. Sandbach, 1907
W. Clarke, 1908-9
Rev. T. W. Sturges, 1912
Sir G. Tyrwhitt-Drake,
            1913 and 1915
C. Thellusson,
            1914 and 1916-19
W. Rice, 1919 and 1938
W. J. Golding, 1920
Capt. R. R. Allen, 1921
R. Fletcher Hearnshaw,
            1922 and 1930
C. Watson,
    1923, 1928, 1932 and 1937

Major T. Potter, 1924
C. N. Goode, 1925
L. Ardern, 1926
Lord Dewar, 1927
Capt. S. W. Clift,
            1929 and 1931
W. Powell-Owen, 1939-52
Capt. E. H. S. Duckworth,
            1953-58
L. F. Outram, 1959
Rev. J. C. Eddy, 1960
H. R. Matthews, 1961
W. Allen, 1962
W. Burdett, 1963
Capt. S. W. Wren, 1964
H. Easom Smith, 1965
A. J. Major, 1966
A. R. Woods,
            1967 and 1969-71
Major C. C. Stevens,
            1968 and 1974
A. Hall, 1972
I. E. J. Kay, 1973

Chapter 7

OPERATION HANNOVER

OPERATION Hannover is the story of an unforgettable experience, which was almost denied me by a much less enjoyable operation — for gall-stones. On 21st September 1971, after several false starts I was entering the operating theatre in Exeter. On 21st October I was entering the boat train for Harwich, *en route* for the famous Young Fowl show at Hannover, in West Germany. This was good going, and I had good cause to make the effort. As with most experiences, the enjoyment of this visit to one of the world's largest poultry shows was immeasurably increased by reason of the fact that it was shared, with twenty-six fellow members of the Poultry Club. In fact, I would regard it as the most wholly enjoyable and worthwhile experience that has come my way in connection with poultry — and there have been many.

In the autumn of 1971, Poultry Club members had been starved for nearly a year of the pleasure that poultry shows bring to fanciers. Because of fowl pest outbreaks among commercial flocks, a total ban on showing our exhibition stock was imposed. Our invaluable secretary, Shelagh Jones, thought that this unwelcome hiatus in our own activities could be offset by organising a Poultry Club party to visit a leading German show. Glowing reports had been brought back by a few members who had been to Hannover Young Fowl Show and other German shows, notably by Major Charles Stevens, our President in 1969 and 1974, who had judged Old English Game bantams in Germany several times.

So Shelagh organised the whole trip, from Harwich to Hannover, via the night ferry to the Hook of Holland, leaving on the night of Thursday, 21st October, and returning to Harwich early on Monday morning, 25th October. Apart from obtaining for us a most advantageous party rate, with train seats and boat berths efficiently booked all the way, she also contacted one of our German members, Herr Charles Stolze, who rallied in the most welcoming way imaginable, as we shall see.

The Party

Having been lucky enough to visit German shows twice previously — Hannover in 1964, and Frankfurt, where the German National was held that year, in 1967 — I knew what a feast lay ahead for the starving eyes of our party.

The party was open to all Poultry Club members, and its final composition proved to be a good cross-section of our membership from all four corners of England, as well as Scotland and Wales. It also covered a wide spectrum of breeds, with the secretaries of several specialist breed clubs in the party, as well as Mrs. Anne Sleap, who was then secretary of The British Waterfowl Association. The party consisted of twenty-seven Poultry Club members, plus three pigeon fanciers who travelled with us to Hannover and back. It was a happy throng.

The Journey

Our first rendezvous was at the boat at Harwich, due to sail at 10 p.m. No party could have got away to a better start. On our arrival at Harwich we were greeted with the news, received from the Ministry of Agriculture that afternoon, that the ban on our own shows was to be lifted. So all of a sudden there we were, setting off, no longer in a spirit of thwarted indignation that our own shows were being indefinitely denied us, but in the comforting knowledge that, after feasting our eyes on foreign fowls, we would soon be taking up the threads of our own activities. This gave an enormous boost to the whole trip, which continued throughout in this happy vein.

We managed to cross the North Sea without, at any rate in my own case, ever setting eyes on a single drop of ocean, leaving dock silently at night, and waking at 6 a.m. next morning already docked at the Hook of Holland, ready to walk across to our train, which left for Hannover direct at 7 a.m. The six and a half hour journey went amazingly quickly. It was a pleasant change to be able to sit and talk with fellow fanciers at leisure, instead of the hurried exchanges that one usually has to be content with during the bustle of our own shows. The journey across Holland and North-West Germany was mostly through flat but pleasant agricultural countryside.

On arrival at Hannover station our instructions were to catch a tram to the eastern outskirts of the city, to the showgrounds, near which our motel was conveniently situated. The driver of the one-man-operated tram was somewhat taken aback when I asked for twenty-seven tickets; but, after some ready-reckoning, we were on our way, distributed in all three sections of the snake-like tram. We managed to alight with a full complement at the appointed stop, whence we were transported in relays in the motel's minibus to the motel, where a wonderful welcome was to begin.

The Reception

Charles Stolze, a well-known Orpington breeder from Rastatt, was there with his son and daughter, who acted as interpreters, and had arranged for Herr Wilhelm Ziebertz, President of the German Poultry Club, to be there to welcome us and to invite us to attend the official opening of the show in an hour's time. We had time to settle into our rooms, and to eat a snack. Then off we went to the opening, which took place in an assembly hall next to the two vast halls in which the show was staged.

It soon became clear that our party was not only expected, but was to be made extremely welcome. After a visitor from behind the Iron Curtain had been called up to the stage and welcomed, it was our turn. As President, I was summoned to shake hands with Herr Ziebertz, the President of the German Poultry Club. This handshake proved no mere perfunctory gesture; it was the cue for a posse of press-photographers to advance and blaze away with their flashlights, and the handshake continued firm and long. Another surprise was in store. Herr Ziebertz, after a most complimentary speech about the gratitude of German fanciers to British breeders, who in the days of the Crystal Palace show, had exported foundation stock of many breeds to Germany, made me, in the name of the Poultry Club of Great Britain, an honorary member of the German Poultry Club. I thanked him on behalf of us for this much-appreciated honour.

Following the official opening, our party was invited across to a private preview of the show, to which the general public was to be admitted on the following two days, Saturday and Sunday. After about an hour, in which everyone's appetite for the feast on the morrow was well and truly whetted, we were bidden to another feast, in a large restaurant in the showground, decorated in Hungarian style, where we were to be the guests of the Hannover Poultry Club at a pre-show dinner.

Here we were further welcomed in a speech from the President of the Hannover Poultry Club, and further honours were bestowed. This time three former presidents of our Poultry Club, Wilf Allen, Will Burdett and Major Charles Stevens, besides myself, were made honorary members of the Hannover Poultry Club, and received badges. This time I felt it incumbent on me to thank our hosts for their great welcome and the honours conferred. I did so in the German that I had learned as a prisoner of war, which appeared to be adequate for the occasion. However, when asked afterwards by one of our hosts where I had learned my German, I replied rather carelessly "In der Gefangenschaft" ("In prison"). This produced rather a puzzled frown, and only when I corrected it to "In der Kriegsgefangenschaft" ("In P.O.W. camp"), was normal bonhomie restored. I haven't repeated that mistake!

The Show

The following morning our party set off for the show. As we neared the showground the scene was more reminiscent of entry to a football match than a poultry show, with queues formed at the turnstyles which clicked briskly. Once inside the showground, we made for the first of two enormous halls. The first sight, on entering, was an array of forty-three "Volieren" — breeding-pens of ducks, large fowl and bantams, consisting of a male and six females, in large well-lit pens.

The first hall also contained the turkeys, geese, ducks and large fowl in single pens. The second hall, which was connected to the first by a corridor, contained the bantams, pigeons and the Youth Section with its 551 entries. In all the numbers on view were as follows:

Turkeys	31
Guinea Fowl	10
Geese	80
Ducks	352
Large Fowl	3,749
Bantams	4,001
Pigeons	5,032
Volieren (43 pens of 7)	301
Total	13,556

To judge this vast quantity of entries, there was a force of one hundred and fifty judges, ninety-eight for the various categories of poultry and fifty-two for the pigeons.

In both halls there was single-tier penning throughout, which gives an indication of the vastness of the total floor space. The halls were like aeroplane hangars. The penning, feeding and watering were first class, and the lighting matched the lay-out. There was much photographic activity, with birds being carted off to the photography room in multi-compartment boxes on trolleys — but not before a card marked "Being photographed" had been placed in the temporarily vacated cage.

The catalogue was on sale as we entered, on the opening morning (Saturday), with every bird's grading and specials marked. With over 13,000 birds to look at, this marked catalogue was a great boon. All the judging had taken place the day before, and the catalogue had thus been completed overnight.

Classes, Grades and Specials

There were no classes as we know them, with first, second, third, reserve and so on. But the entries were grouped together by breeds and varieties, and every single bird received a judge's grading. These gradings were as follows:

V	— Vorzüglich	Excellent
H	— Hervorragend	Distinguished
Sg	— Sehr gut	Very good
G	— Gut	Good
B	— Befriedigend	Satisfactory
U	— Ungenügend	Inadequate
O.B.	— Ohne Bewertung	No assessment
N.A.	— Nicht anerkannt	Not recognised (in the standard)

In addition to these gradings, the more meritorious exhibits were awarded a whole host of specials, including cash specials. The two most coveted awards were the Blaues Band (Blue Ribbon) and the grading "V". At Hannover in 1971 there were 101 winners of Blue Ribbons and 121 recipients of "V" gradings. Both these categories were listed in a sort of Roll of Honour in the catalogue. My view of the merits of this grading system appear in Chapter 8, on Showing. I will merely say here that, apart from the fact that under this system amalgamations and cancellations do not arise, thus enabling any bird entered to appear, the gradings and judges' comments were helpful, both in comparing the merit of the birds and in following the judges' pattern of assessment.

SOME OBSERVATIONS AND COMPARISONS OF BREEDS FAMILIAR IN BRITAIN

In comparing the breeds common to both Britain and Germany, it will be seen that, with few exceptions, our better known breeds were on view at Hannover; some of them, like the Orpington, were in far greater numbers than we can now muster. The most notable absentees were Anconas, Dorkings, Croad Langshans and Old English Game (large). The last three appear in the German book of standards, but the Ancona does not. There is a Mottled Italiener, which is the nearest approach to an Ancona, but it is far removed from the well marked Anconas that we know, with the characteristic "V" tipping. But now to the familiar breeds that were there:

Some Continental Breeds - by Gwenllian Woods

Line 1—Lakenfelder, Augsburger
Line 2—Black Rheinländer, Silver Kraienköppe
Line 3—Golden Kraienköppe, Vorwerkhühner
Line 4—East Friesian Silver Möwen, Silver Brakel

LARGE FOWL

Andalusians (36). These were well laced, with good ground colour. Only moderate-sized combs are wanted. Our best Andalusians are bigger and look more likely layers of large eggs for which the breed is famed.

Australorps (114). I looked them over in company with Clive Bradbury, one of our leading Australorp breeders, and we reached the conclusion that on the whole ours have more size, even allowing for the fact that we were looking at young birds. Otherwise they were similar to ours. A few gipsy faces were seen — and penalised.

Barnevelders (169). Far more popular in Germany than in Britain, in both large and bantam size. One hundred and fourteen Double-Laced, forty-five Blacks and ten Whites were shown, and they were impressive.

Brahmas (66). Fifty-three Lights, ten Darks and three Buff Columbians made a gigantic display of height and size. The Darks were similar to ours, but the Lights were far better than anything we see at present.

Cochins (29). Thirteen Buffs, ten Blacks, three Partridges and three Blues were on view. They were much the same as ours, I thought, and not as impressive as the Brahmas.

Faverolles (24). Of French origin, they are known as Lachshühner in Germany (Lachs meaning Salmon). Besides the Salmon, they are standardised in only one other variety, White. There were twenty large Salmons, of average standard, and four rather disappointing Whites. Alas, there were no Whites among the bantams for Clifford Lowe to compare with the excellent specimens of this variety that he consistently shows.

La Flèche (3). Another French breed which was once familiar, though never widespread, in Britain is the La Flèche, a large black breed with two vertical spikes for a comb. After a long period of oblivion, it has recently reappeared at our shows. At Hannover only three were on view, and they were in the Youth Section. Two of them were graded "very good" and they seemed much like the few that have been shown here recently.

Hamburghs (104) I went round the Hamburghs at Hannover in company with David Kay, our Hamburgh Club secretary, and we were particularly impressed by the Silver-Spangled males, with their length and width of sickle. Their tails were carried at a slightly lower angle than ours. In the females the preference seemed to be for medium-sized spangles, allowing an even pattern, rather than very large spangles which tend to merge into areas of black. The Blacks were smart and slender, with moderate-sized round lobes, well removed from any sign of Minorca type. Gold-Spangled, Gold-Pencilled and Silver-Pencilled were all present, but, as is the case in Britain, they were smaller. Eight moderate Blues appeared in the New Breeds section.

Houdans (18). Similar to ours in type. But they rather lacked mottling, being young birds, which will no doubt brighten up in their second year.

Indian Game (23). Eighteen Darks and five Jubilees. With only a few exceptions, these were taller and less stocky than those that are now winning in Cornwall, and would stand little chance over here.

Italiener (626). These are similar to our Leghorns, but there has been a different emphasis in type. Exaggerated combs and any tendency towards Minorca type and size has been avoided. The breed is in great heart in Germany, as their numbers indicate. Italiener appear in many gay colours, including Silver and Golden Duckwing, Creel, Buff, Brown, Mottled, Barred, Black, White, Blue and Millefleur. The Barred are really barred, and not the more blurred Cuckoo pattern that we know.

Leghorns (83). These were of the American type, such as we would regard as the "utility" type, with much smaller combs and bodies than we see in our latter day exhibition type. They are only standardised in one colour — white. They looked fit and useful but, to me, hardly exciting.

Malays (20). Not having known the Malay in its heyday in Britain, it was hard for me to compare them with those on veiw at Hannover. But I remember being much more impressed by their size and numerical strength at Frankfürt in 1967. But that show was six weeks later in the year, which must have made a great difference in a breed that needs time to develop. Here there were only Light-Red males and Wheaten females, except for a trio of Cuckoos. They were similar to the Malays that we are now enjoying seeing again.

Minorcas (28). Here again, as with the Andalusians and Italiener, exaggerated headgear is not wanted; nor is great size of lobe nor body. I imagine that German judges might regard some of our best as somewhat overdone, whereas we would regard theirs as only moderate for size of body and head. I would think that the optimum lies somewhere between the two types.

Modern Game (16). These appear to be staging something of a revival, for there were none on view at Hannover in 1964. Most of the recognised colours appeared in small numbers — two

Silver-Duckwings, three Golden-Duckwings, four Birchens and a Black-Red. There was some height and reach and type among them There were also two Black females, one of which was rather surprisingly graded Distinguished. A White male was graded Unsatisfactory, with which I concurred, and a trio of Cuckoos were marked "Not standardised". The latter looked most unnecessary to me.

Naked-Necks (22).   Not many people's favourite, but they seemed in good heart, and looked better in a row than one might have expected. There were sixteen Blacks, three Cuckoos and three Reds. Whites were seen in bantam form. They have a few feathers on the head, below which a bright red bare neck leads down as far as the top of the crop before the plumage is resumed. They handle firmly and have a pleasant temperament.

New Hampshire (246).   Not seriously regarded in Britain as an exhibiton breed, the New Hampshre cuts a lot more ice in Germany, as the entries indicate. Two hundred and fifteen Reds and thirty-one Whites appeared, and many of them achieved high gradings.

Orloffs (51).   Orloffs are a distinctive breed of Russian origin. They are in good fettle in Germany. Between the wars there was an Orloff club in Britain, but now they are looked after by the Rare Breeds Society. It would be nice to see more of them, and the Germans have good stock. Thirty-three Spangleds, eleven Mahoganies and seven Whites were penned. The Spangled Orloff is the colour of a Speckled Sussex. They are a muscular, somewhat gamey breed, with full beards and thick necks, and very small walnut combs, similar to that of the Malay They look slightly forbidding, but they are tame.

Orpington (152).   One hundred and fourteen Buffs, twenty-six Blacks, seven Blues and five Whites made up the total. I would say that our best would surpass them for profusion of feather and size. In type they were somewhere between our fluffy heavyweights and the old type Orpingtons. The Blues, though not numerous, received high gradings, and they certainly impressed our Orpington specialist, Will Burdett.

Polands. (a) Holländer Weisshauben or White-Crested (13). There were nine White-Crested-Blacks, mostly good. Two White-Crested-Blues and a White-Crested-Cuckoo also received high gradings. Less impressive was a White-Crested-White, but beardless self Whites have much less appeal than their bearded counterparts.

(b) Paduaner or Bearded Polands (8).   This was a small but fairly complete one-man display. The varieties shown were: Black, Silver-Laced, Gold-Laced, Buff-Laced and Laced Blue

(Andalusian colour). This breed is always easy to fault, the lacing never reaching Sebright nor Wyandotte standard. But all eight were graded "Very good", and two of them won specials. The few Silver-Laced that we see in Britain nowadays are of similar standard to those at Hannover. The others we only seem to see in bantam form

Rhode Island Reds (315).   Without being able to handle them, there was no knowing what the under-colour and wing markings were like. But viewed externally they were a fine display. Length of back and correct tail carriage were conspicuous attributes, as were good combs. There was less tendency to ragged tails in the males than we find. When a breed is bred as widely as this, there is ample room for selection.

Rocks (79).   With thirty-two Barred, twenty-three Whites, eleven Partridge, and ten Blacks, the surprise was the poor showing, both in quantity and in quality, of the Buffs, which mustered a mere three. The Barreds were well barred and of good type and size, with less narrow feathers than ours. The males were a shade lighter than ours. In fact, in all colours the females seemed better than the males, as the gradings confirmed.

Scots Dumpies or Creepers (Krüper) (11).   Although in the German book of standards the origin of the Krüper is attributed to North-West Germany, with no mention of the Scots Dumpy, I could detect only one difference — the lobes. The Krüper has white lobes, whereas the Dumpy's are red. Only Blacks were shown, very glossy and of excellent type and vitality. Despite the lobes, they would be a desirable source of new blood for our depleted stock, I would say.

Spanish (2).   One pair on view, with both birds graded "Very good". But both needed more time to allow their white faces to develop. I met one of the top breeders of Spanish, and he was not showing at Hannover, but waiting for the National at Dortmund. His birds needed more time.

Sultans (3).   Only two were present, and were not as good as Andrew Sheppy's best for wealth of feather in hocks and tail.

Sumatra Game (25).   Dark gipsy faces and horizontal tails were the hallmarks of this breed. They also had the required pea combs, and not the flapping sort of irregular pea comb that we too often see. One cockerel was graded "V" (Excellent), and several others made an impressive display.

Sussex (157).   One hundred and thirty Lights, twenty-two Speckled, three Reds and two Browns, but no Whites were seen. I think that our best Lights would surpass these for size and hackles, whereas the Germans pay more attention to combs and the correct tail carriage.

Welsummers (68). Like its compatriot the Barnevelder, this Dutch breed is far more numerous in Germany than in Britain nowadays, particularly in bantam form. The standard seemed about the same, with nothing placed in the two top grades.

Wyandottes (274). The surprise here, both in large fowl and bantams, was the preponderance of Blacks over Whites. I daresay German breeders would consider our fluffy Whites to have veered too far in the direction of the Orpington type — as do some of our own breeders of the other colours. The Germans have attained short backs and good Wyandotte curves in all the colours. There were seventy-eight Blacks, forty-nine Whites, forty Silver-Laced, thirty-one Gold-Laced, twenty Barred, seventeen Blue-Laced-Golds, fifteen White-Laced-Golds, nine Partridges (CB), six Blues, five Columbians and three Buffs. Points to notice were that in the Gold-Laced and the Silver-Laced the males were what we would consider pullet-breeders; and in Partridges the females were like our cockerel-breeders. The Germans have rejected any standard for which double-mating is required to breed show birds of both sexes. In fact their Partridges are divided into two separate colours (as indeed they really are), our cockerel-breeders being called "Partridge", whereas our pullet-breeders are called "Braungebändert" (Brown-banded). In the laced varieties broad feathers were in favour. The Blue-Laced-Golds and White-Laced-Golds were most attractive and typical Wyandottes.

Yokohamas (5). These were two Red-Saddled cockerels, two pullets and a White pullet. One of the two Red-Saddled pullets joined the elite of the show with the highest attainable grading, the coveted "V". With her beautiful rich colour and her clear spangles, and a long curved tail, she looked good value. It was gratifying to see a good specimen of a rare breed receiving due recognition. The single-combed Phoenix, which we have also called Yokohama, only appeared in bantam form.

BANTAMS

Silkies (32). In Germany Silkies are classified as bantams, whereas we regard them as a light breed of large fowl, and strive for as much size as possible. They would look very insignificant alongside ours, and yet looked rather large and out of place as bantams to our unaccustomed eyes. Thirteen Whites, eleven Blacks and eight Partridges were shown.

Rosecombs (75). Rosecombs are known by the name of Bantam in Germany, after their place of origin on the island of Java. At one time they were known as the Java in Britain, and the name Bantam has been given a much wider use. Thus one has to be careful in speech or correspondence with Germans on the subject of bantams, which are called Zwerge (Dwarfs) in German. The main colour is the Black (thirty-nine), similar to ours. There were also five Whites and seven Blues, with which we are familiar. But the Germans have introduced several other colours into this breed, which, though interesting and novel to us, still lack the type of the Blacks. There were Mottleds, Columbians, Buff-Columbians and Millefleurs.

Sebrights (53). Golds and Silvers in almost equal numbers were shown. Chris Parker, who was then our Sebright Club secretary, found the standard similar to ours, in this well established breed.

Japanese (128). Known as Chabos, they presented a multi-coloured, multi-plumaged display, with frizzled and silkie-feathered variations appearing. The colours seen were: White, Black, Blue, Black-Tailed-White, Black-Tailed-Buff, Mottled, Cuckoo, Grey, Millefleur and Black-Red. It was a display comparable with our annual turn-out of Japanese at their club show at Reading.

Barbu d'Anvers (Antwerpener Bartzwerge) (94). These were present in most of the colours familiar to us, with the addition of Buff-Columbian for the inspection of one of our leading breeders of Belgian bantams, Veronica Mayhew. **Barbu d'Uccle,** as we know them, were not present. Their place was taken by the Federfüssige Zwerghühner (Feather-footed bantams), which we would regard as Booted. They were without the beard and boule of the Barbu d'Uccle and were taller. They appeared in the familiar colours of the Barbu d'Uccle, with the attractive addition of Buff-Mottled, the mottling being white on the tips of the buff ground colour.

MINIATURES

This group contains all the bantamised or miniature versions of the larger fowl, as distinct from the breeds of original bantams in the previous category.

The centre-piece of the whole bantam display was the massive array of 1,091 **Wyandottes,** which appear to hold the place in the German Fancy that Old English Game bantams hold in ours. Of the self colours, as with the large fowl, the 251 Blacks eclipsed the 175 Whites, in quality as well as numbers, in the opinion of two of our leading Wyandotte bantam exhibitors, T. L. Corner and J. Powell. Buffs (twenty-three), Reds (thirty-two) and Blues (twenty-three) were well represented. Of the marked varieties, the Barred (157) were immensely popular and typical, as were the Silver-Pencilled (ninety-one), Gold-Laceed (forty-eight), Silver-Laced (forty-three), White-Laced Golds (thirty) and Blue-Laced Golds (thirteen) were all strong. Twenty-seven Partridge (CB) and sixty-five Braungebändert, sixty-one Columbians, thirty Buff-Columbians and twenty-two Mottled (black-and-white) completed a memorable show within a show.

Of the rest, a glance at the list of entries will reveal that certain of our breeds are far more widely exhibited in Germany than in Britain. This category includes **Barnevelders** (150) and **Welsummers** (170). **New Hampshires,** which we have not yet bantamised, had 128 entries.

Conversely our most numerous breed, **Old English Game,** is nowhere near as widely shown, with only forty-six entries. In fact our **Modern Game** bantams have so far made more of a mark in Germany, with fifty-seven entries of which a Birchen pullet was graded "V" (excellent), and several others were impressive. **Minorcas** were surprisingly few, and **Andalusians** seem to be still emerging. One hundred and eighty-seven Italiener occupied the place of our **Leghorns.** Ninety-four Cochins resembled our Pekins.

I am not in favour of adding to our own breeds, when many of them need all the support that they can get, unless the addition has some intrinsic merit that will justify its inclusion Two such breeds of miniature fowl that I would regard as an asset are the **Kraienköppe** and the **Orloff.** Kraienköppe have already appeared in Britain, and the German standard for them has been translated and adopted by the Poultry Club. Orloffs would have a brighter long-term future in bantam size, I feel, than as large fowl. They looked distinctive, healthy and interesting. Only the Spangled variety appeared as bantams.

SOME OBSERVATIONS ON GERMAN BREEDS OF INTEREST
(See colour illustration)

I do not propose to comment on all the German breeds on show at Hannover, because, with over 13,000 exhibits to inspect, I did not find time to examine all the German breeds thoroughly. But I found the following interesting and distinctive:

Lakenfelder (23). It was good to see this German breed, which has been seen sporadically in Britain for over sixty years, in sufficient quantity and quality to be able to assess them. In males the German standard calls for a white saddle with black ticking on the ends, and lists a wholly black saddle as a serious fault. This could be followed in the judge's gradings. The males with their jet black necks and tails contrasting with their white bodies are unique and most attractive. But for females the standard allows some seemingly unavoidable white at the top of the neck, and this concession detracts from their appearance, compared with the males. Type and tails were excellent. No Lakenfelder bantams appeared.

Vorwerkhühner. These look like Buff Lakenfelders, with buff where the Lakenfelder is white. They were created in Hamburgh and first shown in 1912. Surprisingly they were absent from the ranks of large fowl this time at Hannover, but there were fifteen Vorwerkhühner bantams on view, one of which attained the honour of a "V" grading. Slightly heavier than the Lakenfelder, they represent another unique colour combination, our Buff Sussex being the nearest approach that we know.

Augsburger. This breed comes from Augsburg and the area of the Black Forest, and dates back to 1880. If Augsburgers were to appear in Britain, they might well be taken for large Black Sicilian Buttercups. They achieved fame and attracted attention at Hannover when a pen (one male and six very even females) was graded "V" with a Blue Ribbon, which made it the outstanding pen. They looked very smart with their characteristic buttercup combs. Strangely enough, there were no Augsburgers among the single entries. Only Blacks are standardised, and they don't appear to have been bantamised.

Kraienköppe (66 large and 41 bantams). These have begun to appear at our shows, and, now that they have been standardised in Britain, they could have a future, at any rate in bantam form. They originated from the area of the German-Dutch border, and were first shown in Germany in 1925. Both colours, Silvers and Golds, were shown. With their well rounded tails and their neat heads, with walnut combs and small wattles, they appeared full of potential both as show birds and as layers.

Rheinländer (155 large and 68 bantams). Another flourishing German breed is the Rheinländer, dating back to 1884 in the Eifel area. Blacks are by far the most popular, but Whites, Blues and Cuckoos are also shown. They have magnificent tails and neat heads, with smallish rose combs with the leader following the curve of the head. They have small round white lobes They are of medium size and build, and look decidedly useful, rather like our Black Hamburghs, but with rounder bodies and smaller lobes. The Black males excel in green sheen. They are reputed to be good long-lasting layers, as well as meaty. An impressive breed I thought.

Brakel (56 large and 7 bantams). A row of Brakel females looks for all the world like a row of Campines that we know. But, whereas our Campine males have the same markings as the females, the Brakel male has a silver or gold back and saddle, which makes him a more showy bird. The Brakel is described as being of Belgian origin, but of German development. They were a shade larger than our Campines, from Belgium originally. Silvers outnumbered the Golds as is the case with our Campines.

Ostfriesische Möwen (29).   Fashioned on similar lines to the Brakel, and likewise seen in Silver and Gold, is the East Friesian Möwe, a breed of friendly temperament, which I had known in South Africa but not in Britain. The male is white or gold, with a black tail, whereas the female has a white or gold neck and front, with the rest of its body covered with rows of little black spangles, on a white background in Silvers, and gold in the Golds. They have medium sized single combs like those of our Campines, upright in males and folding near the end in females.

Deutsche Langschan (11 large and 46 bantams).   The German Langshan, like our Modern Langshan, is said to be a development of the Croad Langshan. But the foot-feathering has been discarded, and the result struck me as being like an Australorp on stilts. I found their tall and distinctive type attractive, with no regrets for the missing trousers. Black, Laced-Blue and White are the three standardised colours in large fowl, but in bantams Red, Birchen and Brown-Red are also standardised, though not shown at Hannover in 1971. Blacks were by far the most popular.

Niederrheiner (154 large and 59 bantams).   This is a comparatively recent German breed, bred after 1940 as a quick-maturing dual purpose fowl, comparable to the Marans, but with no claim to the dark brown egg of the latter. Judging by the number on view they must be pretty useful. The colours, like those of the Marans are mostly rather indeterminate, but the "Blue Cuckoo" and the Birchen were the most distinct and the most numerous. The Birchen variety reminded me of the Norfolk Grey, which appeared and seemingly disappeared between the wars in Britain. The Birchen markings on a utility heavy breed body caught my eye.

Deutsche Zwerghühner (131).   This is a popular German bantam breed, with no large fowl edition. It was first shown in 1917, and shows traces of the Phoenix in its make-up. It is of refined bantam size, and appears in many variations of game colours. It has a single comb, white lobes, a slender form and a long well furnished tail.

OTHER BREEDS NOT FAMILIAR IN BRITAIN

Apart from German breeds, there were a few breeds from other countries that we seldom, if ever, see in Britain, but which warrant a brief mention.

Appenzeller Spitzhauben (17).   This is a Swiss breed of very light body. They are silvery-white with small black spangles, much smaller and not as round as those of the Hamburgh. They have strange crests sprouting upwards and pointing forwards, with small horn-shaped combs. One of these made its way to Olympia in 1963, and a few more have been seen here since. They are quaint but too small to attract much attention, I fear, being neither bantam nor large fowl

Bredas (14). This is another light breed of fowl, of Dutch origin. An occasional specimen has reached our shows, but they are virtually unknown in Britain. They have the distinction of being combless. Another hallmark is the vulture hock. They are about the size and type of the Sultan and were on view at Hannover in Black, White and Laced Blue. Distinctive enough, but hardly exciting.

Dominiques (23). This is one of the oldest American breeds. Though it is mentioned in some old poultry books, it is never seen in Britain. Dominiques are a Cuckoo-coloured breed, rather better marked than most. It is a light breed of medium size, with a long body. A neat rose comb with the leader tapering and following the curve of the head, and rich yellow legs enhance its appearance. I found this a pleasing sample of the breed.

Amrocks (59). Another Cuckoo-coloured breed from America. They were like the utility Barred Rocks that we knew, but never really regarded as a show breed. They appeared in fair numbers and good shape at Hannover.

Crève Coeur (2). Two entries, but only one, a rather small female, was penned, in this French breed which once shared a breed club with Houdans and La Flèche in Britain, but seems to be no longer with us. It looks too much like a Black Poland (Bearded), with the kind of two-pronged comb that one tries to eradicate in that breed, to warrant resurrection here.

Shamo Game (15). This Japanese breed appears to be a variation of the Malay, with slightly shorter legs and little or no curve of the back — which latter point strikes me as a commendable modification. It always worries me that, after culling and eradicating roach backs in all other breeds, one suddenly finds oneself having to accept them in Malays. The Shamo beetling-brow expression and colours are similar to those of the Malay.

WATERFOWL

Geese
In the goose section most of our familiar breeds were there — Embden, Toulouse, Chinese (Whites and Greys) and Sebastopol, but no Brecon Buffs nor Romans. German Embdens are more slender about the neck than ours.

A German breed which appealed to me was the Pommeranian, from the island of Rügen on the North German coast and the

Stralsund area. Those on view were all Grey-and-White, but self Whites and Greys are also standardised. The Grey-and-Whites are smartly marked. They are grey across the shoulders and on the back and thighs, with white lacing. The pattern is well defined. The Pommeranian is a large heavy goose, with a shortish back which gives it a compact appearance. It does not have the gullet of Toulouse. Another German breed was the Diepholzer, a lively White goose not unlike the Roman.

Ducks

Vernon Jackson, out noted waterfowl breeders from Wales, had plenty to interest him in the duck section. Again most of our recognised breeds were there, under their own or other names: Aylesbury, Campbell, Cayuga, Crested, Buff Orpington, Indian Runner, Rouen, Muscovy, Black East Indian and White Call Ducks, as well as something very like our Silver Appleyard Bantam duck. There are two types of Pekins, the American utility type and the more vertical German type, with the almost canary coloured plumage that we once knew. The latter were of excellent standard, and would be welcome back here, I'm sure.

The Indian Runners appeared in all sorts of colours. Besides the Whites, Blacks, Chocolates and Fawns that we know, there were some Blues and some of Mallard colour, which was a good feat of breeding, I thought, to link genuine Runner type and height with the bright Mallard colouring.

The Orpingtons were all Buff. What I would have taken for Black and Blue Orpingtons both appeared under the name of Pommeranian, and very smart they looked, with well-defined white bibs. Similarly, when I thought I saw some Welsh Harlequins, they were called Streicher.

A German breed which we do not know in Britain is the Saxony, a gay and attractive composition, bred from the Rouen, Pommeranian and German Pekin, according to the German book of standards, to which it was admitted in 1957. The result is a pleasing creation. The drake resembles a Silver Appleyard male; the female is a harmonious blend of blue and buff, with a line over the eye. They would be a welcome addition to our rather limited list of domestic ducks.

Another composite breed of duck which we saw at Hannover was the Gimbsheimer, even newer than the Saxony. Rather heavier than the Orpington, the Gimbsheimer is blue-grey all over, with no bib. It is named after its place of origin, in the Rhein Palatinate. A handsome duck I thought.

CONCLUSION

On the Saturday evening, sated with the day's feast for our eyes, we were invited to attend a Fanciers' Evening in the Hungarian Restaurant, where we again feasted our stomachs on food and wine and our eyes on the comely cabaret. We were conveyed there and back, apart from those who made a night of it, in a special coach which had been provided for us, and were admitted as guests. Once inside, we were this time allowed to pay our way, which was a relief after so much generosity.

Sunday morning was also spent at the show by most of the party, though a few explored the city of Hannover and its famous Herrenhausen Garden. At three o'clock in the afternoon we left our motel in a cavalcade of Mercedes taxis, led by the motel minibus, for Hannover station. The long journey home was largely consumed in the exchange of impressions amongst each other. I think we all felt that we had shared an experience of a lifetime. There had seemed no end to the hospitality of our German hosts.

However, our gratitude was tinged with embarrassment at the thought that we had a long way to go before we could be in a position to return this hospitality. In a way we were being thanked for what our ancestors had done for the German Fancy in the past. Many of the older German fanciers whom we met still spoke with awe of our wonderful stock at the Crystal Palace. Now the boot was rather on the other leg.

But, apart from the great enjoyment at the time, this visit has, I am sure, benefited our own Fancy in Britain. It showed what can be done when shows are well run, by fanciers for fanciers. The direct result has been the holding of our own Poultry Club National, first at Nottingham in February 1973, and subsequently at Alexandra Palace in the autumn. Let us hope that in a few years time we shall have a National show to which we can proudly invite visitors from abroad. Things are heading that way.

It has been pleasant to record this Poultry Club adventure, which all who were fortunate enough to share will remember with gratitude all their lives. This gratitude goes to Shelagh Jones who organised the trip and offered it to all Poultry Club members, as well as to Charles Stolze and his son and daughter who greeted us with such a welcome, and finally to the Hannover Poultry Club for a great reception to a great show.

Chapter 8

JUDGING

" YOUR NOSE IS CLEAN "

"As a judge, your nose is clean, for a start." This blunt compliment was paid to me by a Northern exhibitor of repute, and I have always tried to keep it that way. It is surely the first basic requirement of judging — to be impartial and oblivious to the ownership of the birds one judges. I often wonder how much a judge is influenced, albeit subconsciously, at dog shows and horse shows, by the fame, sex or appearance of the handler of the dog or the rider of the horse. At least at poultry shows the judge does not have to judge each bird with its owner or handler in attendance. It is true that the owner sometimes seeks to intrude, or otherwise let the judge know which bird is his. But, in my years as a judge, it has not proved difficult to ignore the intrusion or the attempt at identification. Only once have I had to call in the show manager to warn off a persistent intruder who was trying to influence my judging. Blows were only narrowly averted!

As well as a clean nose, it is also vital to have an open mind — open to the merits of all breeds. A judge must constantly fight against having, or appearing to have, favourite breeds or pet aversions. Nor must a judge have his own peculiar fads, which may run counter to the standard, or may result in undue emphasis on one point. He must guard against making a fetish of a particular point of merit, or a particular fault. A balanced, objective judgment should be the constant aim.

HOW TO BECOME A JUDGE

There is no school or course for judges. Nor, as far as I know, is there a manual on the subject, though I once read a book entitled *The Art of Faking Exhibition Poultry*! It was intended, it said, to alert judges to all common, and not-so-common, methods of "improving" fowls for exhibition. In so doing, I fear it was equally liable to alert dubious characters to any methods that they hadn't yet thought of!

So, in the absence of any book of instructions on "How to Become a Judge", it may be of interest and help if I record how I personally became a judge — and, having become one, how I carry out this duty and privilege. I say "privilege" because I regard it essentially as a privilege to be asked to handle, assess and pronounce judgment on other people's birds. Provided that the show is well staged and well run, it is a pleasant privilege, though no sinecure. I say "duty" because I accepted my first and subsequent appointments to judge partly as a duty. Rather as a cricketer or footballer feels he should contribute to the game that he has enjoyed as a player by helping to conduct it for others, as time moves on, so I felt that, after many years enjoyed as an exhibitor, it was right to be prepared to put back something into the Fancy when called upon to judge.

Accordingly, I served a brief apprenticeship as a steward. I think my most instructive stewarding was under Nick Thomas, when he judged all the Soft Feather classes at Launceston in 1961, where most breeds were to be seen. For Hard Feather experience I was lucky enough to steward for W. Jagger at the Royal Dairy Show. After these and a few other useful experiences, I was thrown in at the deep end, at the Royal Cornwall, our biggest summer show, in 1964.

I well remember starting with the two Rhode Island Red classes and being told by my steward, when I had finished, that I hadn't gone far wrong, with the same exhibitor first, second and third in both classes. At least I had been consistent, and when I discovered that the successful exhibitor was Mrs. W. J. Mitchell I felt I must be on the right lines. Next came the Anconas. Again my steward told me that I had the same owner, Edwin Stephens this time, first, second and third. Again I felt good!

But this euphoria was too good to last. Later in the day I found myself in an altercation over my judging of one of the duck classes. I had noticed, with what was fast becoming complacency, that I had again placed a leading duck exhibitor first, second and third out of seven. So the onslaught was rather unexpected. I remember finally telling my assailant to jump in a lake, taking his faulty ducks with him. However, a few years later the same person asked me to judge a show that he was running, so I felt that I had not made an enemy for life after all.

Of course, volunteering to judge is one way of losing friends, I suppose. But someone has to do it, and I didn't feel that this risk was sufficient reason for refusing. Nor should one lose any friends worth having, if one is prepared to admit any mistake that one has made. The judge's decision must be final, but, if you have missed a split wing, it is no use denying that it is split. Nor need your opinion be beyond dispute; provided the approach is courteous, both exhibitor and judge can learn from constructive discussion.

All applications for appointment to the Judges' Panel have to be made to the Poultry Club Council, through the Secretary, who provides the application form. Two personal referees are required, and details of any previous judging and also the applicant's own showing experience are stated. The Poultry Club Council then considers this application.

A well-known and consistently successful exhibitor will normally be appointed to the panel to judge his own breed or breeds. He will normally be required to take a test for other breeds or sections, the test being conducted by a judge of appropriate standing, who reports back to the Council with his recommendation. These tests take place at a suitable show that the candidate is able to attend in his own area.

In my own case, when I applied, in 1963 I think, I was accepted on the strength of success at shows, at home and abroad, with a large number of breeds, as a panel judge for Soft Feather breeds, large and bantams. Three years later, after studying Hard Feather breeds at shows, and at first hand by breeding and showing them, I applied to be admitted for Hard Feather. For this I was required to take a test. I did so at the International under Major C. C. Stevens. The test lasted an hour, and it was one of the most profitable hours that I have spent in the Fancy. Major Stevens not only tested my knowledge of the standards, but also imparted much of his, which has stood me in good stead ever since.

Finally, when in 1974 the Council invited applications for upgrading, in order to give the Panel a more up-to-date appearance, I applied for the necessary extension to include ducks and eggs, thus enabling me to be considered for Panel A. I had judged three British Waterfowl Association club shows, and had been asked to judge a fourth, which was considered good enough. As far as eggs were concerned, all I could say was that, armed with the all-embracing article which S. J. Hawes wrote for the 1969 *Poultry Club Year Book*, I had judged egg classes at shows, without having any of the exhibits thrown at me. This, too, was accepted. So, eleven years after I was first admitted as a judge, I reached Panel A.

HOW TO JUDGE

So much for how to set about becoming a Poultry Club judge. What about setting about judging? In the absence of any laid down instructions on the subject, I can only say what I do.

On approaching a class, I quickly see how many entries and absentees there are. If it is a mixed class, I mark breeds, colours and sexes in my judges book, for possible future reference. Then I start my non-handling inspection. I never dive in and start handling until I have had a preliminary inspection from outside the pen. Diving in too soon disconcerts the birds, and it prevents some birds from showing their type properly. From outside the pen I look for type, outline and general impression. If I like what I see, I put a tick against the bird's number in my book, which means that I shall be handling it in due course.

In this preliminary inspection, I check the head first and then work down the neck, along the line of the back, and then check the tail carriage, giving the bird every chance to carry it well. I make sure that it is not carried to one side. A light tap with the judging stick on the side opposite to that to which it is inclining, will reveal whether the tail has a permanent list to one side or not. At the same time I check stance, look for duck feet, and note the colour and condition of the legs. I find that a routine check like this, in the same order, will ensure that you don't miss anything. Now I am ready to handle those that are in the reckoning for cards. Some may have been eliminated during this preliminary inspection, and it is a waste of time to handle them. No amount of handling will offset a duck foot, a roach back or lack of type. But I make it a golden rule to handle when in doubt, and above all to handle any bird that is in the running for a card.

Now comes the handling. A check on the breastbone as the bird is withdrawn from the pen is my first action. I am careful not to grab the bird in such a way that I damage its wings or tail, which would ruin it for another show. I give it every chance to come quietly with its keel on my hand, as a well trained bird should. Then I check both eyes for sound pupils and correct colour, at the same time examining the lobes and comb further, at close quarters. Then I spread out and check each wing for marking and for split wing, followed by a check on the back for absence of any deformity and on the undercolour. And so to the tail, for texture and for colour, especially at the root of it. In all laced breeds I check the lacing from the top of the neck down to the thighs by raising my knee and spreading the bird across it, keeping the far wing underneath its body, which will prevent it from flapping.

In the course of this handling, some ticks in the book may get changed to crosses. Other birds that handle well may get additional ticks. By now my mind may be made up. If not, one more look at the relevant birds is necessary. But it is no use vacillating, once one has had a thorough check. A decision must now be made.

That is my general routine, but it will be modified as circumstances demand. For instance, if I am judging a class of mixed colours, such as Laced Wyandottes, I may judge them in four groups, all the Gold males first, then the Silver males, followed by the females of each colour. In this way one starts by judging like against like, before eventually deciding between the best of each. The same would apply to a class of Belgian bantams.

Again, if one is confronted with a large class of self-coloured birds, perhaps all of one sex and good even quality, as one often finds in White Wyandottes, Australorps or White Leghorns, it can prove difficult to know where to go after the above-mentioned routine check. There will probably be several birds with two ticks against their names. Extra factors, such as width or texture of feather, state of maturity and fitness, tameness and ability to show well, size and extra emphasis on type, may all help to resolve the final placings.

Finally, as I judge, or failing that, as soon as I can manage, I like to enter a few notes on the birds in my judge's book, which the show provides, partly in case I shall be writing up the classes that I have judged, and partly in case an exhibitor asks me, or writes to me, about his entry. For this purpose, I find plus and minus columns most useful. A bird's notably good points go into the plus column, and its drawbacks into the minus. It saves writing the words "good" or "bad" every time in a limited space, and is concise and easy for reference, provided that one's steward cottons on to the idea quickly.

PLEASURES AND PITFALLS OF JUDGING

My first pleasure immediately after judging is to look at the names on the cards of the classes that I have judged. But this pleasure must be deferred until after the specials, including *Best in Show,* have been decided in conjunction with one's fellow judges. And herein lies one of the greatest pitfalls, in my experience. There exists an understandable but dangerous tendency, which I have found quite prevalent in otherwise sound judges. It is the seemingly irresistible urge to produce the show champion from among the birds that one has personally judged. I have even known a judge to say, when it came to a vote: "I am bound to vote for that one, because I have put it up." To me that is utterly wrong. I will concede that there is some sort of irrational satisfaction when the bird that one has chosen as the best of all those that one has judged goes on to become Best in Show. I suppose in a way it is a vindication of one's choice and judgment.

But it is surely quite illogical to expect the show champion always to come from the classes that one has judged. Therefore it must be wrong to root for one's choice through thick and thin, regardless. Yet I have seen this happen scores of times, and I am only too aware that this tendency needs constant suppressing in myself. I just hope that I succeed in doing so!

Some judges whom I have judged with (no, I did not say "against"!) have been reasonable and open-minded, and mutual concessions have resulted in fair and amicable joint awards of the championships. Others ("game" to the last?) seem to have no intention of shifting their ground. This leads finally to coin-spinning or calling in a reluctant arbitrator to settle the issue — neither of which courses is really satisfactory in the eyes of the exhibitor.

Another pitfall in judging is the attempt to use double standards — one for Hard Feather breeds and another for Soft. To give a concrete example, I will quote from my experience, and it is not by any means an isolated example, either. I have seen Old English Game females, particularly Wheatens, put up for, and sometimes getting, Best in Show with white lobes. When I object, the answer that I usually get is that they could easily be removed! or that they often have them; or that in Old English Game it is shape and handling that matter. Well, to me the standard matters more, and if it stipulates red lobes, I have no intention of tolerating white lobes, any more than I would expect an Ancona with red, or even blushed, lobes to get anywhere.

A pitfall, which I am glad to notice a good proportion of our judges avoiding nowadays, is the tendency to play safe and award top honours to a white or a black bird, knowing that there can be no argument over the markings and little doubt over the colour. I am not advocating the selection of a marked breed merely for the sake of being different, but I have at times felt that some judges play too safe in choosing white or black birds every time. However, in recent years this tendency has become less evident. But it still needs guarding against.

When all the specials have been settled, in one way or another, and these may, if you are unlucky, include some very burdensome "Challenge" classes, my low opinion of which is explained in the next chapter, on showing, you are then free to enjoy your final pleasure — amicable discussions with some of the exhibitors whose birds you have judged. At least, it is a pleasure to do so if the approach on both sides is amicable. A dogmatic or thin-skinned judge is as bad as an aggressive or unconvincible exhibitor.

STEWARDING

A good steward is a great help to a judge, and an indifferent one can be a pain in the neck. Fortunately I have found the latter to be rare.

The first thing I require in a steward is absolute clerical accuracy. With a large number of birds to get through, a judge must be able to rely implicitly on his steward's ability to write down the same correct results on all lists and counterfoils. Not all can, and the ultimate responsibility rests with the judge.

Secondly, one wants a steward who will be ready to handle birds carefully when asked, but will not dive in unasked, thus upsetting the composure of the birds.

Thirdly, though it is nice to have a steward who is observant, it is useless having one who expresses an opinion before one has judged. Comment afterwards is quite all right by me, but never while I am making up my mind. With very few exceptions, I have always had good stewards.

BEST IN SHOW

This most coveted award has made more hackles rise than any other aspect of judging. It is quite surprising how many different snags can arise in its awarding. It is such a popular accolade that any question of doing without it, because of its inherent difficulties, can be ruled out. What is needed, however, is some standard system of its awarding. At all costs those undignified wrangles that have been known to arise, must be avoided. So must the last-minute calling in of a referee, as well as coin spinning, if at all possible.

The problem does not arise at a show judged entirely by one judge. It arises at a show where there are two or more judges — particularly if there is an even number of them.

The system adopted by Reading Bantam show, where there are usually seven or more judges, has been used over a number of years, and is devised to eliminate the bickering, bull-dozing and delays which tend to take place when judges foregather to choose the show champions.

The system operates as follows: Each judge selects the best bird that he or she has judged, and it is placed in a pen alongside the birds chosen by other judges. Then each judge examines all the other birds paraded, and places them in order of merit. The bird scoring the lowest total of points is the winner (the best bird on each list receives one point and the worst receives seven, if there are seven judges).

This method certainly produces a result with no argument. But even this system has its drawbacks. For instance, there may be specialists judging the Pekin, Belgian, Japanese or other club shows, who will automatically bring out birds of their respective breeds. But when it comes to putting the others in order of merit, they may or may not have the necessary knowledge of other breeds. I remember an Old English Game judge, who had brought out a top class Old English Game hen, saying that he knew which Old English Game to nominate, but that he didn't know much about the other six in front of him. Yet he had to put them in order of merit, and the result could be affected by his choice.

Another snag to this system is that with each judge only picking one bird, the choice for Best Opposite Sex might not be truly representative. What if the best male and the best female happened to have been judged by the same judge? It admittedly gets complicated if one reasons too much, and there is much to be said for the harmony and simplicity of the Reading system.

A possible alternative, which also eliminates bickering, and should produce a more soundly based judgment, is to have a panel of experienced all round judges, each with his own section of the show to cover, to select one bird of each sex, and then judge all of them in the Reading manner. This takes care of not only the Best in Show, but also the Best Opposite Sex. But, if this method is used, as it is at the National, care must be taken not to overrule the decisions of other judges. For instance, if a judge has already declared the winning Gold-Laced Wyandotte to be Best Wyandotte, it is no use allowing the Championship judges to select a Silver-Laced Wyandotte for Best in Show. The terms of reference of the Championship judges must be precise, and their choice must only be from birds that are already Best of Breed, if such awards have been made by the other judges.

With that proviso, that is the system that I would like to see in operation at all major shows.

Chapter 9

SHOWING

I KNOW that in life one should endeavour to be an optimist rather than a pessimist. But when it comes to showing poultry, I strongly recommend the reverse procedure. Throughout my years of showing, I seem to have had a sort of protective pessimism, or at any rate a very guarded optimism, which has cushioned me against any disappointments by almost eliminating them, and has made the many exceeded expectations all the sweeter. Better a cheerful pessimist than a dejected over-optimist!

In this chapter, again I propose to review certain aspects of the subject as they strike me subjectively, rather than pontificate objectively. Nor do I propose to write a treatise on the preparation of exhibition poultry. That subject has been admirably dealt with by Harold Easom Smith in his book *Managing Poultry for Exhibition.*

THE PURPOSE OF SHOWING

As far as I am concerned, the main purpose of showing is, I suppose, the production of something of beauty and merit, coupled with the sense of achievement and excitement that success at shows brings. But there are other facets to showing which all add up to form one's motive. For me, participating in, and contributing to, a worthwhile gathering is important. So is the opportunity to compare one's birds with those of other breeders, thereby ensuring that one is breeding on the right lines.

The competitive instinct, or the enjoyment of competing, as distinct from the will to win at all costs, also looms large. But it must not be allowed to loom too large. If a reasonably philosophical outlook cannot be adopted, it is better not to show. Although judging is done according to the standard, there are bound to be differences of personal interpretation and application, and one must be able to accept these.

I can recall a White-Crested-Black Poland cockerel of mine being the Club Show Champion at Olympia, after being cardless in a class of A.O.V. on its previous outing. Similarly, my famous Partridge Wyandotte hen won first at the International after also being totally ignored on her previous appearance. And I am not even saying that any of the judges were wrong. Circumstances alter, and one must take the rough with the smooth.

Conversely, I have had a Blue Frizzle hen adjudged Champion Ornamental at Wadebridge, only to be cardless at her next show, but first again at the next. But here I think peak fitness played a part. I could quote other instances of reversals in my own case, and I am sure other exhibitors could do the same. The point is to be prepared for them. To insure against these reversals, I have always been glad to have more than one string to my bow, when showing. It must be galling to be a specialist breeder of one solitary breed or variety and to have a bad day under a judge, with no hope of compensation elsewhere in the show. I am not advocating too much dissipation of effort, but I can recommend a little diversification as a good insurance against the total disappointment that can await the one-breed specialist on his unlucky day. Thanks to this policy, in my last fifteen years of showing I have only once failed to win at least one first prize — which with my built-in poultry pessimism is enough to send me home happy. The fact that, out of the last thirty-six classes that I entered at six shows, from Ashe House, I won thirty-five, made me even happier.

A very considerable bonus to showing, rather than a motive, is the acquisition of an ever-widening circle of friends in the Fancy. Friendship among fanciers transcends barriers of age, class, politics or nationality. Furthermore the Fancy is by no means a closed shop. Newcomers are welcomed by the Breed Clubs which are affiliated to the Poultry Club. Their support and active participation at shows is vitally needed.

One motive for showing that I have not yet listed is financial gain. There was a time when it was possible for a busy showman to scoop a lion's share of the prize money and make a profit. But nowadays, although it is nice to cover one's expenses, on occasions, with the prize money, there can be very few exhibitors who expect to do so regularly or to make an overall profit. Money can only be an added inducement, but no longer the main incentive. Railage charges and the price of petrol have seen to that.

SHOWMANSHIP

The cardinal attribute of a successful showman must be the ability to plan ahead. Good showmen hatch their chicks with show dates in mind, some six to nine months in advance. Rather like the gardener who manages to grow a constant supply of lettuces, by frequent sowing, so the showman staggers the hatching of chicks, so that fresh batches are coming to their peak throughout the show season.

I believe in constant culling of all youngsters that will not be fit to show, sell, or breed from. This allows maximum space and attention for the others. As the time of the show draws near, so the showman will start selecting his birds. I have found that with frequent handling after dark to tame them, very little penning is necessary. I always keep penning down to the minimum, thus preventing the birds from getting that jaded indoor look that too much time penned-up will cause. I have also kept the washing of the plumage by total immersion to a minimum, contrary to general advice on the subject. I don't enjoy it, and the birds that I have occasionally washed have looked far from enthusiastic in their bedraggled state. But I fully realise that, if you show birds with white plumage, you are bound to wash them to remove sappiness as well as dirt, and I admire the skill and patience of those who are expert in this art. For my part, I soon found that the laced and coloured breeds that I showed were not improved by total washing. The reverse, in fact, was the case, for they seemed to lose their lustre. I preferred to keep my stock as clean as possible at all times, on grass runs, and to wash only as required. The exception to this rule were the crests of the White-Crested-Black Polands, which always benefited from a wash; the Polands obviously could not preen their own crests.

I have always regarded combs and legs as of the utmost importance when preparing birds finally for show, as well as fitness on the day. These points have always seemed to me to be the hallmarks of showmanship.

Another facet of showmanship is the amateur psychology that showmen like to indulge in. It occurs in many forms. I recall remarking to one of our leading Poland exhibitors, Brian Anderton, that the pen number of his show champion, number IIII, was easy to remember. He replied that it was for that very reason that he had put the best of his three entries in that class in that particular pen. He thought he would make it easy for the judge!

But, more seriously, it is advisable to study your judge. I always found it best, when showing Silver-Laced Wyandotte pullets at the annual club show at Birmingham, to enter three. If A. J. Spencer, one of our leading authorities on Laced

Wyandottes, was judging I knew that a soundly laced breast was a *sine qua non,* however pretty the pullet might be elsewhere. I selected my three accordingly. If the judge was previously unknown to me, I would make sure that I included one pullet of the pretty type, which is apt to be less sound on the breast, just in case. I was sometimes glad that I did.

I remember bringing off a minor psychological coup at two successive shows. I was wondering whether to send a Blue or a Black Frizzle bantam female to a show, when I remembered that, when going round the fowls of Ashe, the judge at this forthcoming show had stopped in his tracks whenever he had passed a pen with a black breed in it, whereas he had passed pens containing blues without a backward glance. Acting on this hunch, I sent the Black Frizzle. She not only won her class, but she was adjudged Champion Bantam. A month later the same problem arose. This time the judge was Harold Easom Smith, and I had recourse to his book: *Bantams for Everyone.* In the section on Frizzles he says that some of the best are Blues. I took this as a cue to send a Blue. She duly won an A.O.V. class of nineteen entries. Maybe the Black would also have won any-way — but I enjoyed my amateur psychology!

However, I must in fairness record an occasion when it came unstuck. I won at the International with a Partridge Wyandotte hen, which I gathered was not far off championship honours. My informant, who had added that she would have been his choice, was down to judge at Birmingham the following autumn. So my optimism was a little less guarded than usual this time, as I boxed up the Partridge Wyandotte hen, which was looking her best. When I got to the show, I found her cardless in a strong A.O.V. class. It was quite a chastening experience! But she won the following year, under a judge whom I had not bothered to psycho-analyse!

TROPHIES

I fully realise that my attitude to trophies and cups is not shared by everyone but this seems the place to express it. It always strikes me as very silly when press photographers tell the Wimbledon tennis champion or the winners of the F.A. Cup to kiss the trophy. It seems an unnatural thing to do.

As for cups won at poultry shows, I can't work up much enthusiasm for them either. In fact the winning of a floating cup often entails a financial loss to the winner. The cup may have to be posted back at the end of the year during which the winner is allowed to keep it. Before that, money may well have been spent on having it engraved. Cups vary in appearance, and not all of them are elegant and decorative; but all of them require frequent polishing. They need insuring, by the club or society to which they belong, and this in turn may lead to the further expense of valuation. Cups have even been known to lead to litigation, which, even if successful, can involve some hefty expenditure of club funds.

In my opinion the club money spent on the postage, ever-rising insurance, periodical valuations and the engraving of cups and shields, would be put to better use in helping to finance the annual club show.

When it comes to a cup to be won outright, it is a very different matter. But even here my outlook is utilitarian. I prefer tankards or spoons, or anything which can be used, as well as providing a frequent pleasant reminder. Accordingly, whenever I am consulted or am donating, my choice is always a tankard or spoon, and never a cup or shield.

Rosettes have many advantages over cups as awards for high honours at poultry shows. At least they are non-returnable, and don't need cleaning nor insuring, nor sending by parcel post. But they are getting increasingly expensive, and, after a brief parading, mine all end up in the large box which contains all my cards and Blue Ribbons as well. They brighten up the show, when first awarded, and I am always grateful to receive them.

But for me, the prize card is the great thing. They can be easily stacked, and produced for reference, or for nostalgia. If one has the desire, and suitable wall space, they can be affixed and displayed. In my possession I have many attractive cards, but none more so than those awarded by the Royal Dairy Show, particularly those very substantial cards with white imprinted lettering on a black background, awarded for Best of Breed. Many other shows have attractive cards, and this is where I personally would concentrate a club's main allocation of funds for awards.

In short, I would advocate the swiftest possible phasing out of all floating cups from shows and from balance sheets. In the former they incur multiple expense to the club and actual financial loss to the so-called winner; in the latter they are apt to be listed at their insurance or replacement value, whereas their realisable value, if sold to raise funds, is usually far lower. Non-returnable tankards, spoons, rosettes and cards are sufficient reward for me, and much less bother for club secretaries.

CHALLENGE CLASSES

Whereas I am all in favour of special prizes, to be awarded in addition to the normal class prizes, such as Best of Breed, Best Ornamental, Best Hard Feather, Best Soft Feather, Best Lady's or Best Young Exhibitor's Exhibit, and other additional honours which bring further interest and pleasure, I abhor so-called Challenge classes.

The reason for my abhorrence of Challenge classes is twofold; as a judge and as an exhibitor. As a judge, it can be a very long and exhausting task, after a full morning's judging of one's classes, to have to confer with other judges in order to sort out all the possible candidates for the various Challenge classes. The first point to emerge, usually, is that many of the good birds are not entered, which immediately debases the value of the whole gruelling exercise. Judges have to lead each other round the likely birds that they have judged, brushing past exhibitors who are wanting to discuss things with them. At a big show this can take a lot of time and energy, which would be far better spent in constructive discussion with exhibitors and the general public.

From the point of view of the exhibitor, the Challenge classes present an unwelcome dilemma. To enter all one's birds raises the total entry fee for the show rather drastically for such a dubious honour. To enter the bird that you personally rate highest, and then find that the judge has preferred one of your others, which you have not entered, is too galling a risk to take. For this reason, many exhibitors leave the Challenge classes alone, and that is why they are apt to be so meaningless, apart from the chance of some small monetary gain to the lucky few.

Having stated, in no uncertain terms, my own dislike of Challenge classes, it is only fair to add that there exists a point of view of the organisers of shows, and as without them there would be no judges and no exhibitors, it is only fair to state it. Challenge classes, despite the dislike that I have mentioned, undoubtedly bring in some much needed revenue. The fact that they draw some support must indicate that they appeal to some exhibitors. As far as bringing in revenue is concerned, I feel that an overall slight increase in entry fees is a sounder alternative. As far as their popularity with some is concerned, I think that, though winning a Challenge class may sound very grand, it is in reality an empty honour that should not be encouraged. I don't, touch wood, envisage the day when we shall have a judges' strike over Challenge classes, but I think my fellow judges will have a greater expectation of life if Challenge classes are replaced by less tedious and more meaningful specials. I am glad to say that many show committees have already reached this conclusion.

GRADING CARDS

Having poured derision, first on floating cups, and then on Challenge classes, it will be a welcome relief to discuss something for which I feel the greatest enthusiasm, namely judges' grading cards for all exhibits, whenever feasible — which isn't often, I realise.

The system of grading, which is used with conspicuous success and efficiency on the Continent, has been introduced at our National at Alexandra Palace. It has in no way replaced our traditional competitive system of comparative assessment (first, second, third, etc.). But it has been used to complement it.

Obviously there has been much variation in the efficiency of its application, in the early stages. But I personally welcome it as a worthwhile addition to our existing prize card system.

The Judge's Grading Assessment cards used at the National have six possible gradings: A — Outstanding; B — Very Good; C — Good; D — Satisfactory; E — Unsatisfactory; F — No Assessment. A tick is put against the appropriate grading, or else the five inapplicable gradings are crossed out. Half the card is left available for any comments that the judge may wish to make. An exhibitor can learn a lot about his own birds, and about the judge, from these cards.

From the exhibitor's point of view, it can be reassuring to know that your bird which has perhaps been placed only third or lower, has none the less been graded B (Very Good). The judge's remarks, too, may prove helpful for one's future breeding, and for future reference when showing under that judge.

I can illustrate these points from recent experience of my own. At the 1974 National, I showed a Black Frizzle bantam pullet, at her first show. She was placed second to my Blue Frizzle, but what pleased me still more was that she was graded A (Outstanding), with the judge's comment: "Lovely feather. Presses the winner hard." This was most reassuring, and was amply borne out when she won next time out.

On the other side of the coin, I showed an Andalusian bantam hen, in the absence of anything better available — a fox had upset my forward planning by demolishing in one night the whole brood from which my October show birds should have come. In her youth she had won a class of nine Andalusians at Reading. But at Alexandra Palace she received the modest grading D (Satisfactory), and the remarks: "White in face. Seen better days. Quite dark enough." This taught me that the judge knew his business, and that I should have known mine. I did really. It was my dislike of empty pens that clouded my judgment in sending her. But I was grateful for the card.

From the judge's point of view, an ignorant or woolly remark in his comment may well expose him. The fear of this should put him on his mettle, and if he is up to his task, he will welcome the challenge.

However, I would not advocate replacing our first, second, third method by the Continental grading system, because I would be sorry to see this element of excitement disappear from our shows. It is the combination of the two that I advocate, thereby getting the best of both systems.

Grading cards are only feasible at shows where the judges have sufficient time to apply them properly. Obviously at one-day shows, with each judge covering a large number of classes, there is no time for grading cards. But at two-day shows, like the National, where judging is spread among a large team of judges, I feel the grading system is well worth applying and perfecting.

TRANSFER CLASSES

I want to mention Transfer classes, because both as a judge and as an exhibitor, I have detected a certain amount of antipathy towards them, as well as some incorrect application. To me, they are something which should be treated seriously and administered correctly, for they are a means of upholding a very fundamental rule of showing, namely that no bird should ever be denied the opportunity to appear at a show simply because of the lack of other people's entries. The Transfer class is designed and incorporated in the Poultry Club's show rules, for this very purpose. Its correct use is vital.

In the Poultry Club Show Rules, revised in 1967, it states in paragraph 4, under the heading "Cancellation of Classes":

". . . No breed, variety or colour scheduled in cancelled classes may subsequently be transferred to compete under 'Any Other Variety' or 'Any Other Colour', but can compete if a class is specially provided as a 'Transfer' class. Show secretaries are asked to put a note in schedules requesting exhibitors to state whether they agree to birds being so transferred in the event of breed classes being cancelled."

Under the protection of this rule, entrants in "Any Other Variety" or "Any Other Colour" classes make their entries in the knowledge that under Poultry Club Rules, no breeds or varieties from scheduled classes can be transferred to A.O.V. or A.O.C. Whether the schedule reserves the right to make these transfers or not, if the show is held under Poultry Club Rules, such a transfer is not allowed.

The correct transfer is to a Transfer class, and not to A.O.V. nor A.O.C. The Transfer class thus upholds the cardinal rule that no bird shall be denied the right to appear, but it must not do so to the detriment of the entrants in the A.O.V. or A.O.C. classes. There is no earthly reason why the Show Champion should not come from the Transfer Class. It is perfectly respectable.

SHOW ORGANISERS

There are over a hundred show holding societies affiliated to the Poultry Club of Great Britain, which means that there are a lot of very public spirited and energetic show organisers to whom the Fancy must be profoundly grateful. In this particular field of human endeavour a very great deal is owed by the many to the few.

I think that events of the last decade have amply revealed that fanciers' shows, run by fanciers for fanciers, are by far the best to support and attend. Furthermore, with commercial shows becoming unreliable and fewer in number, fanciers' shows have become a vital necessity, up and down the country.

The most notable examples of this are, of course, the two National shows that have come into being in England and Scotland. The chief credit for the former goes to two outstanding fanciers and show organisers, Will Burdett and William Parr. Will Burdett it was at the crucial Poultry Club Council meeting, when the whole venture hung in the balance, who tipped the scales by volunteering to be show organiser of the pioneer Poultry Club National show at Nottingham. This show demonstrated what could be done by Poultry Club initiative, with no help from, nor dependence on, the commercial poultry industry.

William Parr, as President of the Southern Counties branch of the Poultry Club, came forward to run the next Poultry Club National at Alexandra Palace. It needed men of their calibre to launch this far-reaching development of the Fancy, and to them a very great debt of gratitude is due. This extends to those members who have rallied with practical and physical help, particularly at penning and unpenning time. Likewise, we are also indebted to our secretary, Shelagh Jones, whose work has been notably and voluntarily increased, not only by the swollen membership that her own efficiency has brought, but also by her volunteering to handle much of the secretarial and financial side of the show.

The news that the Scottish branch of the Poultry Club has also staged its own National is particularly welcome. Thanks to the work of the President, J. Barr, and the Secretary, J. McGarva, and the Scottish show committee, fanciers in Scotland now have their own National show. This is eminently satisfactory for them in view of the fact that they are debarred from joining in at Alexandra Palace by the fowl pest regulations of the Scottish Ministry of Agriculture, whereby no fowls leaving Scotland are allowed back.

There are many other show organising secretaries and committees throughout the country, on both sides of the border, to whom our gratitude is due. Thanks to their efforts, we have learned to cease being dependent on other people's shows, where our presence was apt to be somewhat on sufferance. Thanks to our voluntary show organisers, we now run our own.

PERSONAL HIGHLIGHTS

Seeing that this is largely a personal poultry book, and in view of the many thousands of words I have written on other people's birds, I am allowing myself the privilege of recording just a few of the highlights of my showing career at its height. I have put it at the end of this chapter on showing, so that anyone allergic to a little trumpet-blowing can move on to the next chapter without more ado. In any case I will ration my indulgence and won't keep you long!

The first that springs to mind is the winning of four of the main championship prizes, over a period of three consecutive years, with my laced breeds, at Birmingham, where the best birds from all over the country converge. They were: Champion Large Female in 1968 and 1969, with Silver-Laced Wyandotte pullets; Reserve Champion Large Male in 1968, with a Gold-Laced Wyandotte cockerel; Reserve Champion Large Male in 1970, with an Andalusian cockerel.

The second highlight was the International show at Olympia in 1969. It was the last to be held, and also my best. It brought me six first prizes, as well as the Champion Large Male (White-Crested-Black Poland); the George Isherwood cup for the Champion Breeding trio (Gold-Laced Wyandottes); and the Ludovici Trophy for the best team of birds shown by one exhibitor, based on the percentage of points won from points possible.

Highlight number three was also in 1969, at the final Royal Dairy show, when my birds won all nine of the single bird classes in which they were entered, and in six of these classes the runner-up was also mine. In fact, out of the fifteen birds sent, only one (my third string Silver-Laced Wynadotte pullet) was beaten by anyone else's bird. My breeding trio of Andalusians had to be content with second place to A. J. Major's renowned Silver-Grey Dorkings, which was no disgrace; but my Andalusian cockerel registered a major breakthrough for the breed by appearing among the show Champions, to round off a memorable day.

The fourth highlight was a rather similar near clean sweep, this time at The Rare Breeds Society's club show at Congresbury, near Bristol, in 1972. Again I entered nine classes and won them all. Again, of the twenty birds sent, only one was beaten by any-one else's. Of these, a Dark Brahma cock was Show Champion, and a Blue Frizzle bantam hen was Champion Bantam. This was the first time that I found myself handing back half my prize money!

My fifth highlight relates to my swan song, just before retiring from Ashe House in 1972. In the first half of that year, out of thirty-six classes entered, at six different shows, thirty-five were won.

Finally, a mere Southerner's record at Northern shows gives me a quiet chuckle. Out of six birds sent North of Birmingham, all six came back with first prizes: in 1966, two Buff Rocks at the Northern at Harrogate (yes, Will Burdett was not showing — he was judging); a White-Crested-Black Poland cockerel came back in 1969 from Harrogate with a first along with an Andalusain cockerel similarly rewarded; and a Partridge Wyandotte hen and another Andalusian cockerel completed a successful trip to Ribble Valley show in 1968. Mind you, I took care not to send likely losers on these missions! I have too much respect for Northern fanciers.

That is the end of the trumpet-blowing. Now I derive vicarious pleasure from the successes of others, especially with my former breeds. Thank you for bearing with me — if you have!

Chapter 10

RARE BREEDS

A RESCUE OPERATION

RARE breeds of poultry were officially invented in the summer of 1969, when Andrew Sheppy, an enthusiastic and go-ahead young fancier at Congresbury, near Bristol, decided that concerted action was needed to save many rare breeds from imminent extinction.

Accordingly, he wrote a circular to many breeders of rare breeds, and I was delighted to write an article outlining his project in the now defunct *Poultry Fancier*. I also readily agreed to be the first president of the society. By the end of the year, Andrew Sheppy had mustered over a hundred members, and as early as January 1970 the first Rare Breeds Society club show was held, in the Canning Town Hall, in conjunction with the West Essex Bantam Club. This proved to be quite an historic occasion. There were breeds there with their own classes for the first time in decades, such as Spanish, Lakenfelders, Yokohamas and Old English Pheasant Fowl. In all, there were 127 entries in 20 classes for Captain Duckworth to judge; care was taken over the staging, even to the extent of providing double-length pens to accommodate the tails of the Yokohama males, and it was voted a great success.

By the next club show, which was boldly held on its own at Congresbury in February 1972 (fowl pest regulations had ruled out any club show in 1971), there were over 200 entries, with some really excellent stock on show, judged by Ian Kay. An interesting display, with far-reaching results, was a gathering of fifteen Araucanas, large and bantam, with a view to comparing the existing stock of this breed and getting it standardised as

*Dark Brahma cock. Rare Breed Society club show champion, 1972.
Brahmas are no longer a "Rare" breed, since a club for them
was re-formed in 1973*

soon as possible, thus enabling Araucanas to compete at shows as well as laying blue eggs at home. The upshot of this was that, thanks to the persistence of Mrs. D. Roxburgh, Araucanas were standardised by the Poultry Club in 1973, and were able to appear, in classes guaranteed by their new breed club, at the next National show, and elsewhere. This was no mean achievement.

The third Rare Breeds Society club show was held at the Poultry Club National at Nottingham, judged by Wilf Allen, in February 1973. In October of the same year the Rare Breeds Society guaranteed classes at the National at Alexandra Palace, which, though not a full club show, was a tour de force for Rare Breeds. And so to February 1975, when George Drake and I shared the judging at the club show at Congresbury. This time, despite the departure of Araucanas, Brahmas and Cochins, there were 171 birds in twenty-seven classes, with some interesting resurrections of breeds previously "missing, presumed dead".

Apart from these club shows, the holding of which is one of the Society's main functions, classes have been obtained at many other shows all over the country, and special prizes have been provided.

DEFINITION OF "RARE"

So much for the establishment and progress of The Rare Breeds Society, as far as club shows are concerned. Before we go any further, it is essential to define a "Rare" breed. The definition decided upon by The Rare Breeds Society is: "Any breed which lacks an operative breed club". The operative word here is "operative", because there were, and may well be in the future, inoperative breed clubs, in that they failed to hold an annual club show or an annual general meeting, and had virtually ceased to function, though they existed in name. Occasionally a breed is endangered by a dormant or ailing honorary secretary, who will neither get on nor get out. In these cases the protection of The Rare Breeds Society is extended to breeders of the breed in question. Several breeds have been helped in this way. Conversely, some breeds, under the protection of The Rare Breeds Society, have flourished to such an extent that its breeders have felt in a position to form or re-form a breed club. They are perfectly free to do so. So far, there have been four instances of this: Dorkings (Hon. Sec. — Mrs. Belyavin) in 1970; Cochins (A. A. Roskell), in 1972; Brahmas (D. W. Ledward), and Araucanas (Mrs. D. Roxburgh), both in 1973. This is an admirable state of affairs, and a few other breeds may conceivably emerge and stand on their own feet.

The Rare Breeds Society caters only for rare breeds, and not for rare varieties of breeds which have breed clubs to look after

Red-Saddled Yokohama cock. Champion Large Fowl at the 1970 Rare Breeds Society club show

Lakenfelder cockerel. A winner at the Royal Cornwall and at Yeovil
Photo — "The Field"

them. For example, Silver-Pencilled Hamburghs, Blue Minorcas or White Dorkings to give three examples of rare varieties, as opposed to breeds, are all looked after by their respective breed clubs. There is no encroachment, nor need of any, here.

Thus The Rare Breeds Society's definition of a "Rare Breed" is perfectly workable, and some initial muddles at shows, caused by ambiguous schedules, and doubts among exhibitors, seem to have been eliminated by now. The important thing for show organisers to remember, when drawing up the schedule, is to list Rare Breed classes above Any Other Variety classes. (We have used the term "Any Other Variety", when we mean "Any Other Breed", for so long now that it would prove difficult to break the habit). If Rare Breeds have a class, they have no business to appear, additionally or alternatively, in the A.O.V., any more than a Leghorn can, if there is a Leghorn class. It is very simple.

The other point that needs watching is the list of breed clubs which is published every year in the *Poultry Club Year Book*. These breeds, and any other breeds known to have a breed club but not affiliated (this applies to Old English Game fowl at present), will not be eligible for Rare Breed classes. All others will.

THE BREEDS

The Rare Breeds Society conducted a census in January 1975 of rare breeds now being kept by its members. Based on this census, the following breeds can be expected to appear at shows. Nearly all of them have done so within the last five years:

> Andalusian, Appenzeller Spitzhauben, Aseel, Brabanter, Burmese Bantam, Campine, Croad Langshan, Derbyshire Redcap, Frizzle, Houdan, Ixworth, Jersey Giant, Kraienköppe, La Flèche, Lakenfelder, Malay Game, Marsh Daisy, Modern Game (large fowl only — the bantams have their own breed club), Modern Langshan, Nankin Bantam, New Hampshire, Norfolk Grey, North Holland Blue, Old English Pheasant Fowl, Orloff, Phoenix, Rumpless Game, Scots Dumpy, Shamo, Sicilian Buttercup, Spanish, Sultan, Sumatra Game, Transylvanian Naked-Neck, Tuzo Bantam, Vorwerk, Yokohama.

N.B.—To these must be added the Auto-Sexing breeds which have thrown in their lot with the Rare Breeds Society.

Then there are other previously known breeds which don't appear to exist in Britain at present, according to the census.

These breeds fall into two categories:

> 1. *Foreign breeds* which might conceivably re-appear: Belgian Game, Booted Bantam, Breda, Bresse, Crève-Coeur, Malines.

2. *British breeds* which appear to have become extinct, and seem unlikely to re-appear:

Buff Medway, Coveney White, Golden Essex, Wherwell, Wyndham Black, York, Yorkshire Hornet.

These breeds were mostly created between the two World Wars and none of them ever became at all widespread. Frankly, and with apologies to their originators, they do not appear to be much lamented. Nor do they warrant a description. It seems far better to devote energy to the perpetuation of other more successful British breeds, such as the Dorking, Sussex, Orpington, Derbyshire Redcap, Scots Grey, Scots Dumpy, Old English and Modern Game, and "Indian" Game — or "Cornish", as the Americans more rightly call it. All of these were here long before, and have already out-lived, their less established compatriots.

STANDARDS FOR RARE BREEDS

The standards or descriptions of Rare Breeds may be found as follows:

(a) Full standards published in *British Poultry Standards,* 1971 revised edition.

Large Fowl

Andalusian	Jersey Giant	Redcap (Derbyshire)
Aseel	Malay	Scots Dumpy
Bresse	Modern Game	Spanish
Campine	Modern Langshan	Sultan
Croad Langshan	New Hampshire	Sumatra Game
Frizzle	North Holland Blue	Yokohama
Houdan	Old English	
Ixworth	Pheasant Fowl	

Auto-Sexing breeds:

Brockbar	Dorbar	Welbar
Brussbar	Legbar	Wybar
Cambar	Rhodebar	

Bantams

Andalusian	Houdan	Malay
Frizzle		

(b) Other breeds briefly described in *British Poultry Standards*, 1971 revised edition.

Large Fowl

Crève-Coeur	Marsh Daisy	Phoenix
Le Flèche	Norfolk Grey	Sicilian Buttercup
Lakenfelder	Orloff	Wherwell
Malines		

Bantams

Booted	Nankin	Sumatra Game
Campine	Rumpless	Yokohama
Croad Langshan		

(c) Breeds which have been officially standardised by the Poultry Club since the publication of *British Poultry Standards*, 1971 revised edition, and published in the *Poultry Club Year Book* as follows:

1973
Nankin Bantams

1974

Brabanter	La Flèche	Sicilian Buttercup
Burmese Bantam	Norfolk Grey	Transylvanian
Crève-Coeur	Orloff	Naked-Neck
Kraienköppe	Rumpless Game Bantam	

All the above standards were submitted to the Poultry Club Council by the Rare Breeds Society. In most cases old standards were unearthed. In others the standards of the country of origin were translated. It is expected that the standards for further Rare Breeds will in time be submitted to the Poultry Club for official sanction, and for publication as soon as passed.

This work on the standards by the Rare Breeds Society is proving very helpful to breeders of rare breeds and to judges alike.

THE FUTURE OF RARE BREEDS

Predicting a future is usually a rash undertaking, and to predict a rosy outlook for our rare breeds of poultry would be fool-hardy and wishful. But it can be said with certainty that their outlook is far brighter now than it has been for many years — as long as the Rare Breeds Society remains well led and well supported. The slippery slide towards extinction has been halted, and in some measure positively reversed. But the ground gained

Unbeaten Andalusian cock
First at the International, Royal Dairy, Devon
County and South of England shows

Andalusian hen
A Royal Cornwall, Devon County and Yeovil winner
Also dam of three consecutive Royal Dairy winners

Photo — "The Field"

could so easily be lost, if apathy or lack of support were to ensue. Now is the time to consolidate a promising start, and to build on solid foundations.

This must be done by those interested in the survival of worthwhile breeds created by our ancestors. And it must be done by lovers and keepers of poultry. There have been attempts, of varying duration, by agricultural, scientific and zoological organisations to establish "gene banks" of certain breeds of poultry, which in my experience did not match theory with practice. The right people for preserving our breeds of poultry are poultry fanciers, and the right sphere for their activities and for their encouragement is within the Fancy.

However, having said that, it is pleasing to record some recent satisfactory liaison between Andrey Sheppy and The Rare Breeds Survival Trust. In 1968 the Royal Agricultural Society and the Zoological Society of London set up a working party to look for ways and means of preserving British farm animals. Their research resulted, in 1973, in the setting up of The Rare Breeds Survival Trust. The intention was initially to concentrate its efforts on sheep, cattle and pigs, with the hope of doing something at a later date for horses, goats and poultry. As early as 1975 The Survival Trust has begun to implement this latter hope, by allotting money towards the survival of the Scots Dumpy. This is a most welcome form of encouragement, which the Rare Breeds Society hopes to utilise to the full.

I would like to see the Scots Dumpy revived and perhaps gain for itself a reputations as a sitter and brooder of ducklings and pheasants in zoos and pheasant farms throughout the country, replacing the crossbreds and mongrels now in use. I found them really suitable for rearing ducklings, at Ashe, with their low clearance. In addition, there is no reason why Dumpies should not be bred, by selection, as quite passable layers — which brings me to a basic principle of Rare Breed preservation, namely intrinsic merit.

I do not favour, nor advocate, the preservation of rare breeds just for rarity's sake. I seek intrinsic merit as well. I shed no tears for the "mushroom" breeds which sprang up between the wars, and never really caught on. I urge the preservation of the older and more traditional breeds, which are fortunately still with us in reasonable quality, with scope for improvement, even if economic circumstances have drastically and dangerously reduced their quantity. I also urge the encouragement of a few interesting arrivals from the Continent, such as the Kraienköppe, provided that they have intrinsic merit. I emphasise that I do not advocate a proliferation of unthrifty breeds — but I do urge tolerance, especially by all judges, of other people's choices.

The rarest of the rare at Ashe—
a Spangled Orloff pullet, a Russian breed

Fanciers who can only see the merit of their own chosen breed, and even profess contempt for other breeds, will never make fair judges.

BANTAMISATION

One further point on the subject of rare breeds is the question of bantamisation. At present at a Rare Breeds Society club show, the large fowl outnumber the bantams in the ratio of three or four to one, which is the reverse of the position of most shows that cater fully for both large fowl and bantams. The reason for this is that not many of the rare breeds of large fowl have been bantamised, and nearly all breeds of which exist only in bantam form, such as Sebrights and Rosecombs, have their own breed clubs, and are thus not "rare".

At a time when every effort is needed towards increasing the number and improving the standard of the existing rare breeds of large fowl. I hesitate to recommend simultaneous efforts at bantamisation. But it might be argued that, with ever-rising costs of feed and railage, the fowl of the future, nay the present, is the bantam, and that to survive, a breed should really be bantamised. Equally, it might be argued that we have an ample selection of bantam breeds, "rare" and otherwise, as it is, and that efforts at preservation are best directed at our large fowl. This could well be valid for the present, but on balance I feel that bantamisation should be the ultimate aim for most breeds, particularly for those whose large fowl size is big enough to allow a reasonable contrast. A good example of this is the Andalusian. In 1972 there was only one Andalusian bantam at the Rare Breeds Society club show. By 1975 there were nine Andalusian bantams, staged on top of nine large Andalusians, and a most interesting and creditable comparison they made.

I feel that other breeds would do well to follow suit. For example, Spanish, Sumatra Game, Red-Saddled Yokohamas, Lakenfelders and La Flèche are all suitable and distinctive enough for bantamising. Malays, Frizzles and Kraienköppe are already with us, and Orloffs and Phoenix are just across the Channel in good bantamised form. Spasmodic efforts have been made with Campine and Houdan bantams, but perseverance such as some of our earlier bantamisers, like W. F. Entwisle, displayed early in this century, is needed. The Rare Breeds Society is now in existence to encourage this necessary perseverance. It is vital that the Society be given active and sustained support.

Chapter 11

CONCLUSION

THE cardinal rule of speech-making is, I have been told, never to start with an apology for the fact that you are about to make one. I agree. Accordingly, at the start of this book I decided to dispense with an introduction, and to plunge straight into what has amounted to a personal story of involvement with the wonderful breeds of poultry.

Consequently, as I reach the place for the conclusion, I find that I still have a few things to say, which might have been in an introduction, had there been one.

This book has been largely a personal story, and although I have endeavoured to moderate the use of the first person singular, I feel that an apology is due to anyone who has nevertheless found it excessive. However, I also wanted to avoid the sometimes rather forced use, or over-use, of "one". So, if I have used "I" too much, one apologises!

The book is, of course, to a considerable extent, auto-biographical, or rather, poultry-autobiographical. The pursuit of poultry has clearly played a major part in my life — probably too major! But languages, travel and active participation and interest in many forms of competitive sport have all had their share of attention. I hope that a one-track mind has been avoided — if only narrowly!

My main aims in embarking on this book have been three-fold. First, I have aimed to give pleasure. Just as I set up the Ashe House Poultry Breed Preservation Centre on lines to suit myself, and hoped that enough people would approve to enable us to carry on, so likewise, in writing this book, I have written mainly to please myself, and hope that in so doing I have pleased a fair number of my readers. This policy worked at Ashe — let's hope that it has worked again, and that pleasure has not only been derived by me, but also given to others.

Secondly, after writing many articles on poultry for *The Field, Poultry World, Poultry Fancier, Fur and Feather* and the *Poultry Club Year Book,* many of them illustrated, I felt the urge to contribute an illustrated book to the literature of poultry. In doing so I have not sought to imitate the great illustrated poultry books of the past, such as those of Harrison Weir, Lewis Wright or Stephen Hicks. Nor is it intended as a manual on poultry-keeping — though I hope that the reader will feel that an assortment of knowledge has been gleaned by reading it. My purpose has been to entertain.

My third aim is the most important, and that has been to stimulate interest in the keeping of poultry for pleasure, and in particular in the preservation of our breeds. I sincerely hope that, at least in some measure, I have succeeded in this aim. If, perchance, I have even managed to inspire the establishment of another Poultry Breed Preservation Centre, such as my wife and I ran at Ashe, then I would feel that an ultimate goal had been reached. Who knows?

By way of final conclusion, I feel that anyone who has stayed with me thus far is entitled to know why I brought to an end such a seemingly successful and enjoyable era as ours at Ashe House. The answer is simple — advancing age. During our time at Ashe, and indeed for the whole of my schoolmastering career before that, we had both remained remarkably fit and healthy. But my attack of pancreatitis, caused by gall-stones, and the subsequent operation for the removal of the latter, served as a timely warning that we could not both expect to continue healthy and active for ever. So we decided to retire when all was going well and under control. Our last season open to the public was our best, and our final show season was also the most successful. It seemed the right moment to retire. What is more, we have done so with sufficient time and energy to enjoy an active retirement.

I have not completely weaned myself from keeping poultry. On the wooded Devon cliffs, five miles away from Ashe, I have continued with some experimental breeding which I had started at Ashe, and wanted to pursue further — the establishment of Andalusian bantams and the creation of a strain of Buff Frizzle bantams. In other words, in a small way, I am practising what I have preached in my last chapter, on the bantamisation of Rare Breeds. I still find it absorbing.

Of course, if we were to let ourselves do so, I'm sure we could easily miss our life at Ashe House, which was an era of great fulfilment. But good things are apt to come to an end, and we have filled the gap with other interests, and with two wonderful holidays —

a visit to my wife's relations and my former colleagues in South Africa, and also the realisation of a lifelong ambition to see the Canadian Rockies. When the immigration officer at Vancouver airport asked me the purpose of our visit, I replied unhesitatingly: "To see the Rockies." No elaboration on this was needed. Anyone who has seen them would appreciate that there could be no more unquestionable purpose.

Finally, retirement has meant time to devote to the writing of books. I hope you have enjoyed this one!